OUR LIVING WORLD OF NATURE

The
Life
of the
Ocean

Developed jointly with The World Book Encyclopedia

Produced with the cooperation of
The United States Department of the Interior

The
Life
of the
Ocean

N. J. BERRILL

Published in cooperation with
The World Book Encyclopedia

McGraw-Hill Book Company
NEW YORK TORONTO LONDON

N. J. BERRILL *was born in England and holds degrees from the Universities of Bristol and London. He has taught in England at the Universities of London and Leeds and in Canada at McGill University in Montreal. From 1937 to 1947 he was Chairman of McGill's Zoology Department and from 1947 to 1965 was Strathcona Professor of Zoology. His extensive researches in marine and developmental biology have taken him to many parts of the world, and he has worked at marine biological laboratories in France, England, the West Indies, Canada, and the United States. Dr. Berrill is a Fellow of the Royal Societies of London and Canada, and he has written nearly one hundred research papers, several professional books, and many magazine articles. He is also the author of a number of books for the lay reader, including the prize-winning works,* Man's Emerging Mind *and* Sex and the Nature of Things. *Dr. Berrill resides in Swarthmore, Pennsylvania, and is currently at work on a new book.*

Library of Congress Catalog Card Number: 66–29822

1234567890 NR 721069876

05025

Contents

WINDS OVER THE OCEAN 9

Mother Carey's chickens 10; Round-the-world navigators 12; Masters of the air 13; The high-diving boobies 16; Fish that fly 18; Surface sailors 20; Currents of air and water 20; A sea of weeds 24; The great eel mystery 28; Other migrating fish 30; From salt water to fresh 35; A ribbon of life 36; How currents are formed 41; Drifters from the shore 42

BELOW THE OCEAN'S SURFACE 45

Plants that wander 46; Manufacturing with light 47; Living light 50; One-celled fishermen 51; Ocean food chains 52; The herring's changing diet 54; The swimming larvae 56; Transparent predators 58; Arrowworms and comb jellies 60; Jellyfish 63; Colonial swimmers 64; Oceanic swimmers 66; The bony fishes 70; The sharks and rays 74; The whales 81; The migrating plankton 88; Why does the plankton migrate? 90; Life in the depths 91; Eyes in the deep 93; Living flashlights 95; The mysterious false bottom 100

THE BOUNTIFUL OCEAN 105

The arrival of spring 106; When summer comes 110; The late blooming 111; Deserts in the sea 112; The rich cold oceans 113; Lush sea pastures in the Antarctic 114; The pyramid of life 118; The world's largest animals 123; A sea of penguins 127; The Antarctic upwelling 130; The Humboldt Current 133; Clouds of birds 134; Red tides 136

THE OCEAN FLOOR

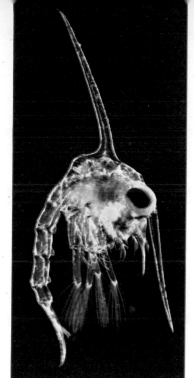

*Forests of kelp 140;   Sea otters 144;   The magnificent
coral reefs 145;   Coral's partnership with plants 149;   Where
corals flourish 152;   A coral-reef park 155;   The coral-reef
community 166;   The giant clam 174;   The octopus 177;
Life on the continental shelf 177;   Bottom feeders 180;
Many filtering techniques 181;   Starfish—enemies of oysters
and scallops 182;   The undersea plains 185;   Clams—
creatures of the shallow sea 185;   A dangerous ability 186;
The burrowers 187;   Predators of the sea floor 188;
The problem of growing up 190;   In the deepest water 192;
The history of the world 195*

APPENDIX

*Ocean Life and Our National Park System 202;   Endangered
Ocean Animals 206;   Sharks and Their Relatives 208;
Mammals of the Ocean 211;   Man in the Ocean 214;
Keeping Ocean Animals in the Home 217;
A Walk along the Shore 222*

Glossary 224
Bibliography 227
Illustration Credits and Acknowledgments 228
Index 229

Winds over the Ocean

Go down to the sea and watch the waves rippling or pounding along the shore and feel the sea wind in your face. Sea gulls peck at whatever washes up or else sit idly on the beach with their heads to the wind so as not to get their feathers ruffled. Busier than the gulls, the smaller black-capped terns dive at the ocean surface for fish and rise with a fluttering, water-shaking beat of wings.

Climb to the top of a cliff, the higher the better, and look down. There you may watch gulls soaring upward from the water below, or gliding to and fro, in the mass of rising air that flows up the cliff. The upward draft does all the work, just as an escalator carries you upstairs, and the gulls have no need to flap their wings at all.

Whenever the wind blows against a slope, whether the slope is a cliff or the side of a wave, it moves upward and can lift a bird if its wings are outspread. Even when there is little wind, the steep waves or breakers advancing toward the shore continually push and lift the air in front of them. Pelicans make use of the air movement by gliding in formation close to the breakers, and in this way they can travel for long distances without a single wing stroke. Even at the height of a great storm, these heavy, powerful birds can be seen proceeding up and down a line of breakers with the same calm and measured flight as they employ in the finest weather.

Across most of the great world ocean, far out of sight of land, the wind blows, sometimes fitfully and sometimes steadily. Only rarely, except near the equator, does the wind cease long enough to leave the sea a glassy calm. Among the birds, only master fliers or master swimmers can live on the open ocean. Some of these are small birds, and some are among the largest birds of all.

Mother Carey's chickens

In summertime, if you take a short cruise out to sea off the Atlantic coast, you are likely to see storm petrels skimming and darting close to the water. Known to old-time sailors as "Mother Carey's chickens," the storm petrels are the most oceanic of all birds. One of them, Wilson's petrel, has the appropriately oceanic scientific name of *Oceanites oceanicus*. Flying with rapidly beating wings, Wilson's petrels look very much like swallows, with a distinctive patch of white above the base of the tail. If you could follow them for a year, you would find them breeding on the barren, remote islands of the Antarctic Ocean, then flying north across the equator, heading for the Gulf Stream. They reach Cape Hatteras, off North Carolina, about the middle of April and almost immediately invade the mild waters along the Atlantic coast as far north as Labrador. In this way Wilson's petrels escape the harsh Antarctic winter and enjoy the warmer part of the year in both the Northern and Southern Hemispheres.

Wilson's petrels dance and flutter about the ocean surface, fishing for small crustaceans. No larger than our backyard songbirds, storm petrels are thoroughly at home in the open sea, even in bad weather.

But they pay a heavy price, for they must fly as much as ten thousand miles twice a year. Furthermore they travel most of the way well out of sight of land. How such birds keep their general direction while searching for small fish, crustaceans, and squid to eat has been puzzling naturalists for many years.

Except when breeding, storm petrels rarely touch land. They use the ocean surface for their place of rest as well as their source of food. Such small oceanic birds exert their mastery over wind and water with their small but powerful

The fork-tailed petrel (*top*) and Wilson's petrel (*bottom*) are both storm petrels, a term that applies to about twenty different species. Wilson's petrel enjoys two distinctions: it is the smallest of all the ocean birds, and it is the most abundant bird on earth.

wings and paddling feet. They also take advantage of the shelter of waves when the seas are rough, skimming so low that they remain most of the time within the trough of the waves. You can hardly see them from the deck of a ship. Only when the ocean is calm and silvery are these birds silhouetted plainly against it. When they feed, they often seem to stand on the water, facing the wind with their wings held out rigidly. Their webbed feet paddle fast in the water to hold their places. Even during a strong gale these almost weightless creatures manage to move forward without obvious effort.

Round-the-world navigators

The large oceanic birds need huge wings to support their bodies. You would find the wandering albatross a breath-taking sight, with its wingspread of ten or eleven feet. It generally glides on outstretched wings rather than beating the air. Unlike some petrels and other birds that migrate across the equator, the albatrosses keep mostly to the cooler, windier regions south of the equator. But they may journey several times around the world in the course of a year. Everyone who has ever seen the albatross in flight, particularly the wandering albatross, has been lost in wonder. An ocean traveler, S. W. Hutton, voyaging in the far-southern ocean about a century ago, described the wanderer:

Nearby, in the morning sunlight, flew the long-anticipated fowl, even more majestic, more supreme in its element, than my imagination had pictured. It was mature, all white and black, doubtless an adult male. As it turned and turned, now flashing the bright underside, now showing the black that extended from wrist to tip on the upper surface of the wings, the narrow planes seemed to be neither beating nor scarcely quivering. Lying on the invisible current of the breeze, the bird appeared merely to follow its pinkish bill at random. The albatross remained with us only a few minutes, but at noon the same bird was back again, covering tens of miles of water in the swift wide circles. . . . When banking, it sometimes tilted to an angle of 90 degrees so that the lower wing cut the water, and it may well have used the great webbed feet more than the stubby tail in steering. It was a curious sight when the albatross prepared to alight under our stern, and then, changing its purpose, ran heavily across the water for fully a hundred paces before the wings could raise the large body again into the air.

Like the largest airplanes, the albatross finds takeoff the hardest maneuver in flying. An albatross sitting on the water, fishing for squid or shrimp in calm weather, will try to avoid a ship by swimming rather than by making the great effort of taking to the air. Even with a swell of water and rising air currents, an albatross with a ten-foot wingspread may have to run along the surface of the sea for several hundred yards, hitting the water with its wings, before it becomes airborne between one swell and the next. Even so, it seldom rises higher than the deck of a large ship. Yet in the belt of the west wind in the southern ocean, where the wind rarely ceases to rage tumultuously, the great wings of the albatross are in their element. The wind and the wanderer circle the earth together. One wandering albatross followed a ship for well over three thousand miles. (Actually the bird flew many times that distance, when its long sweeps from side to side across the sea are taken into account.)

The speed of the wandering albatross is astonishing. On a windy day the great white bird may appear on one horizon, wheel by, and disappear toward the other, while the watcher stands spellbound aboard his ship. The albatross is the king of the air as it rides the sea wind.

Masters of the air

Most oceanic birds are islanders, since they all nest on land and many need islands also for resting. One in particular has a habit, strange for a sea bird, of never landing on the water. Naturally, it must remain near land at all times. The magnificent frigatebird, or man-of-war bird, ranks with the wandering albatross as a master of the air. But whereas the albatross needs cold, dense air and winds blowing across the ocean to support its weight, the frigatebird is built to soar in the lighter air of the warm tropics. Seldom out of sight of land, it roosts at night on the tropical islands and shores around the world, in the Atlantic, Pacific, and Indian Oceans. During the day, it soars to considerable heights by riding upward on the warm column of air that rises from an island as soon as the sun comes up. When men were exploring the oceans in small sailing ships or in outrigger canoes, they watched for frigatebirds, whose presence always meant that land was close. The Polynesian islanders and the traders and missionaries took the birds with them on voyages and re-

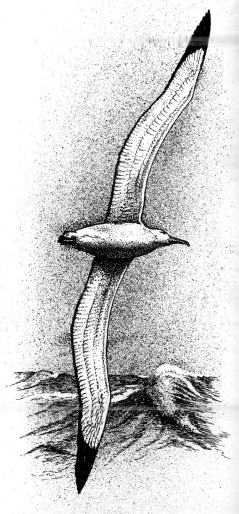

The largest of all flying birds, the wandering albatross has long symbolized the vastness and solitude of the open ocean. This bird spends the first five or six years of its life roaming tens of thousands of miles through the world's cool southern oceans. Then it instinctively returns to its ancestral breeding grounds to mate.

leased them with messages to fly back to the islands from which they came.

Though impressively large, frigatebirds are smaller than albatrosses. Their wingspread reaches seven or eight feet instead of ten or eleven. But in proportion to the size and weight of their bodies, their wings are larger than those of the albatrosses, and so are the powerful breast muscles that operate them.

Notorious robbers, these birds often snatch prey from other fishing birds, particularly the boobies. Nevertheless

they probably catch most of the fish that they eat on their own. Sometimes you will even see frigatebirds overtake and capture flying fish. They plunge toward the sea with a hissing sound and deftly seize the prey in their hooked beaks, without getting their feathers wet. Because they have no oil on their feathers, they must remain dry: water would soak them at once, and they would never rise again.

In any case they cannot take off from the water, and even on land they must launch themselves into the air from the height of a bush or tree.

With his brilliant red throat pouch, the male frigatebird cannot be mistaken for any other bird. The pouch is air-filled and can be inflated and deflated at will; when puffed out, it feels like a warm blown-up toy balloon. In place of the male's finery, which is displayed only during the breeding season, the female frigatebird shows only plain white breast feathers. The young are brown-black with white heads and underparts sometimes streaked with rust color.

An ungainly creature on land, the frigatebird is as agile as a swallow in the air. The great spread of wings, supporting a body weight of only three pounds, permits the bird to respond to the slightest shift of wind and air current. Notice the hooked beak, a perfect instrument for snapping up a jellyfish or shrimp from the surface of the water—or for snatching a freshly caught fish dinner from another bird!

The high-diving boobies

Both boobies and frigatebirds are true creatures of sea and air. The boobies' broad webbed feet are designed for swimming on or beneath the surface of the sea. Boobies also dive, but unlike frigatebirds they do not hesitate to get their plumage wet. They go straight into the sea to seize fish with their beaks and often swim a considerable distance below the surface, remaining submerged for some time. An eyewitness report of the remarkable fishing technique of the boobies was left us by an early visitor to the Galápagos Islands, on the equator in the eastern Pacific:

> These birds collect together in small flocks for the purpose of diving. They fly around in a circle and continue to rise till they get to the heights of from sixty to a hundred yards in the air, when one of them makes a pitch to dive, at which

16

motion every one follows, and they fly down with remarkable swiftness, till within four or five yards of the surface, and then suddenly clasp their wings together and go into the water with the greatest velocity that can be conceived of, exceeding anything of the kind that I have ever witnessed. . . . They go into the water with such force as to form a curve of thirty to forty yards in length before coming to the top again, going to a great depth under water. They glide under water at almost as great a degree of swiftness as when flying in the air.

If you should be nearby when boobies and frigatebirds are fishing, keep a sharp watch as a booby rises from the water, heavily laden with the fish it has caught and swallowed under the surface. Suddenly a frigatebird swoops down on the booby and causes it to throw up its fish. The quick frigatebird, a much better flier, seizes the prize in midair and carries it off.

All kinds of boobies dive deeply on occasion, but when there are enough flying fish around they seldom need to do so. They are experts at catching these fish, which usually swim near the surface. You will find red-footed boobies busily engaged in catching flying fish wherever they abound, provided that there are nearby islands. Wherever the boobies are, there will be the frigatebirds also, engaged in fishing and in robbing the boobies of their catch.

The red-footed booby is a frequent victim of the frigatebird's aerial piracy. It is normally restricted to the world's tropical waters, but a violent storm occasionally carries a stray individual as far north as the Gulf coast. If you sight a largish ocean bird in this region and it has bright-red webbed feet, you can be certain that you have come upon one of the rarest visitors to our shores.

Fish that fly

Like frigatebirds and boobies, flying fish are true creatures of the warm seas and tropical breezes. From four to eighteen inches long depending on the species, they feed on crustaceans and other small forms of life in the upper level of the ocean. By peering into the clear tropical water, you may be able to observe that the flying fish in turn are continually threatened by larger fish, and to a much lesser degree by sea birds such as the booby.

Most of the time a flying fish swims underwater. To take to the air, it drives toward the surface. You may notice that it is spurred by the onward rush of a fast blue-water creature, such as a dolphin or bonito, which would like to make a meal of it. Watch how the flying fish folds both pairs of fins against its body and, as it breaks through the silvery mirror of the surface, spreads out its great pectoral fins to support the front part of its body. It taxies on the water, propelling itself violently with its tail, particularly the long and strong lower lobe. As the fish gains power, its whole body shakes and the tips of its pectoral fins vibrate, giving a false impression of rapidly beating wings. The little fish shoots into the air at a speed of at least thirty-five miles an hour, much faster than it can move through water, spreading its pelvic fins and lifting its tail from the water. Now it glides rigidly. Time the flight and you will realize that it rarely lasts more than half a minute or extends more than three hundred yards. But keep watching, for at the end of a flight the flying fish may lower its propeller tail and work up enough speed for another takeoff.

Even very young flying fish can fly in this way for short hops. Francis Fletcher, a preacher and adventurer, who accompanied Sir Francis Drake on his round-the-world voyage of the *Golden Hind*, wrote:

> The increase of the flying fish is such that their fry do cover the face of the seas where they have spawned, which being of the bigness of gnats do sometimes scud upon the superficies of the water and sometimes instead of flying do skip from place to place like grasshoppers, practicing that being young which they must use when they be old.

Flying fish do not actually fly, but simply glide on their wing-like pectoral fins, attaining speeds as high as thirty-five miles an hour. They are attracted by light, and sometimes come soaring in through an open porthole at night. Flying fish share their peculiar form of locomotion with certain species of squid, which take to the air in somewhat the same fashion.

One of the flying fish shown here is fully airborne, while the other is building up to takeoff speed with powerful strokes of its tail.

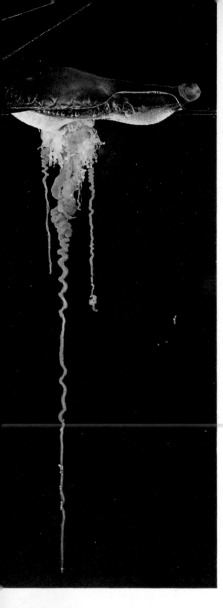

Surface sailors

Besides birds and flying fish, animals that sail on the surface make use of the wind, particularly in the warmer oceans. Two of these, the subject of writings from earliest times, will certainly catch your eye by their beauty and color. To this day they are known by the names given to them by Elizabethan sailors: the Portuguese man-of-war and the sailor-by-the-wind. Marine biologists know them as *Physalia* and *Velella,* respectively. Of all the soft-bodied drifters of the seas, the sailors-by-the-wind have captured the mariner's imagination to the greatest extent. They are related to the jellyfish but are much more complex. Seen from a small sailing ship, these creatures are entrancing. Sometimes you will find them covering the ocean as far as the eye can see, each one a little blue-purple disk, a couple of inches across, with myriads of small anemonelike mouths hanging below. Each hoists a sail above the disk to catch the breeze, to go wherever the wind blows it.

The Portuguese man-of-war is a similar but larger living sailboat. It cocks its gas-filled blue-pink balloonlike sail at an angle to catch the wind, dragging its stinging tentacles as much as a hundred feet behind. Often when the wind has blown these creatures toward a tropical or semitropical shore, they may become stranded on the beaches by the thousands. Anyone who handles or steps on them will soon discover that the terrible sting remains long after the creature is dead.

Beautiful but deadly, the Portuguese man-of-war is abundantly supplied with stinging tentacles (shown contracted here) that employ a nerve poison chemically related to cobra venom. A full-grown specimen has a sail eight to twelve inches long, and it can capture, kill, and devour fish of mackerel size.

Currents of air and water

The winds of the world are important not only to oceanic birds but to the life within the ocean as well, for they drive the sea before them. In northern and far-southern latitudes prevailing winds blow from west to east, producing ocean currents that flow in an easterly direction. Around the Antarctic, where no land blocks its way, a great eastward-moving cold current known as the West Wind Drift goes round and round. Closer to the equator the winds and currents go mainly from east to west. However, just north of the equator, the warm air over the ocean rises almost straight up, and there is no constant wind at the surface. This is the region known as the *doldrums,* where sailing ships in former times were often becalmed for days or weeks, while the crews suffered greatly in the hot, breezeless air. Yet north and south of the doldrums lie the sailor's friends, the trade winds. They are the steadiest winds on earth.

The first man to study and understand to some extent the nature of trade winds and their importance in creating the great ocean currents was William Dampier, a pirate, a naturalist, a navigator, and at times a gentleman. He roamed the oceans for forty years during the late seventeenth century.

Dampier showed that the trade winds blow from the northeast in the Northern Hemisphere and from the southeast in the Southern, and that they drive the ocean before them. In both the Atlantic and Pacific Oceans the trade winds create the great currents that would encircle the globe if there were no land barriers. The North Equatorial Current and the South Equatorial Current sweep westward from the bulge of Africa to Brazil and from the Pacific coast of Central America to the East Indies and beyond. In the Atlantic, water from both the North and South Equatorial Currents flows toward the West Indies. Some of it skirts the islands on a northward path, but most enters the Caribbean Sea and the Gulf of Mexico. This tremendous mass of water forever flowing westward and piling up in the Gulf must go somewhere, and it can escape only by flowing out again on a northeasterly course between Florida and Cuba. This is the origin of the Gulf Stream. As it moves on, following the line of the Atlantic coast, it eventually swings out across the ocean, this time in an easterly direction toward the continent of Europe. Ocean currents such as these have strongly influenced much of the life of the ocean as well as the ways in which men have crossed the seas.

The exquisite little sailor-by-the-wind is closely related to the Portuguese man-of-war, but its sting is much less potent and it feeds on smaller prey. Both animals are completely passive drifters, traveling wherever wind and current take them.

LABRADOR CURRENT

NORTH ATLANTIC

NORTH PACIFIC CURRENT

GULF STREAM

CALIFORNIA CURRENT

CANARIES CURRENT

NORTH EQUATORIAL CURRENT

NORTH EQUATORIAL CURRENT

EQUATORIAL COUNTERCURRENT

SOUTH EQUATORIAL CURRENT

SOUTH EQUATORIAL CURRENT

BRAZIL CURRENT

HUMBOLDT CURRENT

WEST WIND DRIFT

WARM CURRENTS

Ocean currents flow through the sea like great rivers, often differing markedly from the surrounding water in temperature and mineral content. The two prime molders of the currents are the winds and the rotation of the earth, but a host of secondary influences are at work, too—tides, heat absorption and radiation, land barriers, bot-

tom contours, rainfall, and evaporation. The total effect of these factors is shown in this map: a complex system of interacting water masses that is only partially understood by oceanographers.

If we leave the scientists to struggle with the details, the general principles of current formation

OCEAN CURRENTS OF THE WORLD

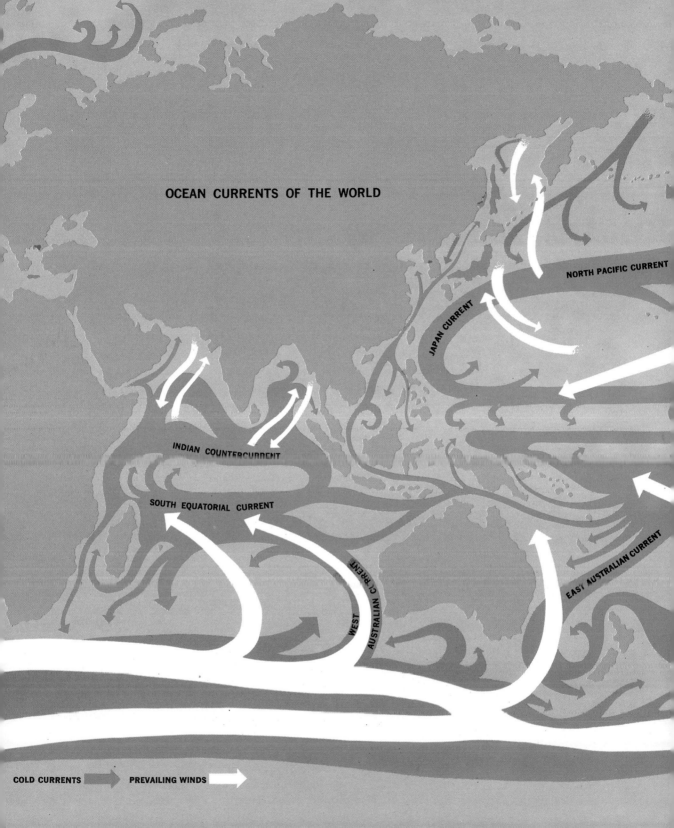

NORTH PACIFIC CURRENT

JAPAN CURRENT

INDIAN COUNTERCURRENT

SOUTH EQUATORIAL CURRENT

WEST AUSTRALIAN CURRENT

EAST AUSTRALIAN CURRENT

COLD CURRENTS ➡ PREVAILING WINDS ➡

are not hard to grasp. The trade winds blow diag
onally toward the equator in both hemispheres,
driving the water steadily from east to west, in
the great globe-encircling system of Equatorial
Currents. But when one of these currents encounters a barrier of land, such as the eastern coast
of South America, the current must deflect north
or south, or both. Now the earth's rotation comes
into play, in the form of the *Coriolis force*, which
causes northbound currents to veer to the right
and southbound currents to veer to the left. The
result is the vast clockwise current systems of the
Northern Hemisphere and the counterclockwise
ones of the Southern Hemisphere.

A sea of weeds

Sargassum weed, shown here about twice its actual size, derives its name from the Portuguese word for a kind of grape—a reference, no doubt, to the little air bladders that keep the plant afloat. The weed propagates both by branching to form new fronds and by fragmentation. In general, plants that flourish in the open ocean are of microscopic size; sargassum is the sole exception.

When Columbus set sail westward from Spain to discover a new route to the Far East, he first headed south to the Canary Islands before turning west into the great unknown. From there he was on his own, looking in the sea and the sky for some indication of what might lie ahead. One of the first things he saw was some seaweed floating by with a crab attached, suggesting that shore was close at hand. He wrote in his journal that "everyone was pleased, and the best sailors went ahead to sight the land first." What he did not know was that his ships were only about halfway across the Atlantic. Nor was he aware that they were caught in the westward sweep of the North Equatorial Current and would cross the ocean whether they had wind or not.

The weed was a sign, but not of land. Columbus was seeing for the first time something then unknown to Europeans, for he was skirting the edge of the Sargasso Sea, a great sea of floating weeds in the open ocean. The Sargasso Sea is actually an enormous eddy of slowly turning water in which the sargassum weed grows, drifting slowly around the center. The edge of this great spinning wheel of water in the North Atlantic Ocean is formed by currents: the great sweep of the Gulf Stream to the north and east across the Atlantic, the Canaries Current flowing south along the eastern side, and the driving North Equatorial Current flowing from the bulge of Africa to the West Indies.

Not only is the weed no sign of land, it is not even a sign of shallow water, for the sea floor lies almost four miles below. The sargassum weed gave rise to dark legends that ships get caught in it, finally to rot and sink, but it is rarely dense enough to impede the progress of a ship. Nevertheless the weed is one of the mysteries of the sea, and it supports a fascinating variety of living creatures.

Sargassum is a yellow-brown seaweed commonly found throughout the tropics, attached to rocks and dead coral reefs in shallow water. The leaflike fronds of the weed float because they have small air bladders. From time to time some weed is torn away from its anchorage by storms and

This well-camouflaged crab is a lifelong resident of the Sargasso Sea. As an adult it is a nonswimmer, yet the clumped sargassum weed is the firmest ground it ever knows. If it loses its grip on the weed, it will sink to its death in the eighteen thousand feet of water beneath.

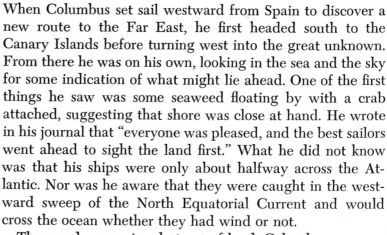

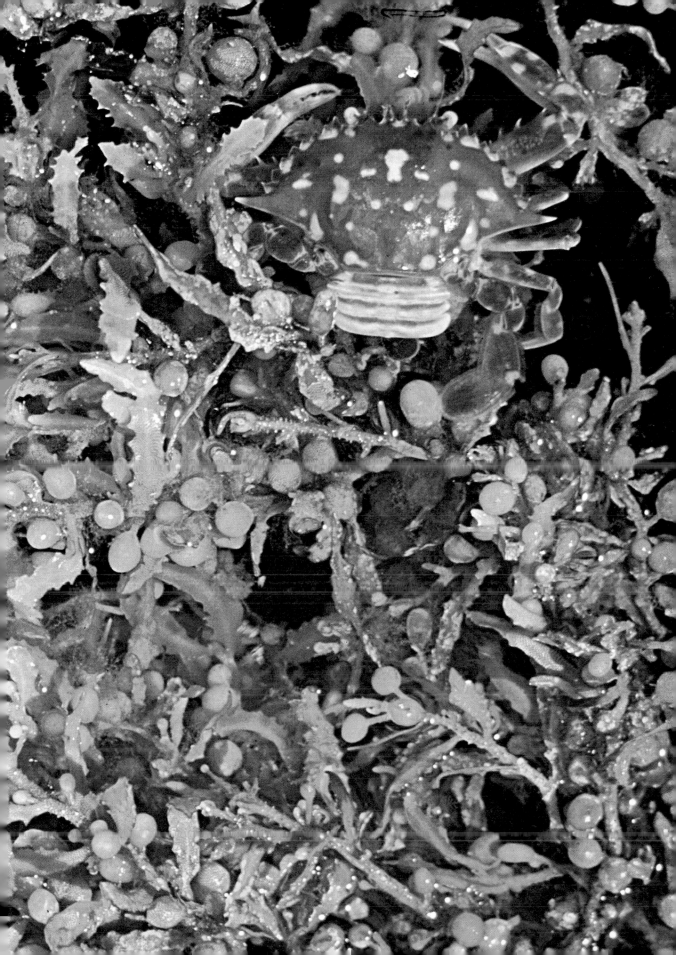

drifts wherever the currents take it. Weed from the Gulf of Mexico is swept along with the Gulf Stream and deposited in the Sargasso Sea. There it finds a new home, joining whatever has gone before. Sargassum gets along without the rootlike holdfasts that other seaweeds need to attach to rock or mud. It floats with its built-in buoys and continues to grow as a floating weed. Altogether, it is estimated that about ten million tons of sargassum drifts endlessly within the limits of the Sargasso Sea.

You can get an idea of just how ancient this world of floating weed may be by examining the creatures that inhabit it. Most of them resemble the weed so closely in color and form that their species must have lived there for hundreds of thousands of years. They also show the same coastal origin as the weed itself, for most are similar to the animals found in the shallow sea close to shore. Of course, they have changed to some extent in adapting to their new abode.

Altogether about sixteen different kinds of animal life make the weed their home. There are tubeworms, hydroids, sea mats, sea squirts, and barnacles. Other creatures, free to move around, are even more interesting. The sargassum sea slug, for example, is a snail without a shell. Its soft, shapeless brown body is spotted with dark circles and fringed with folds of skin. It is so well camouflaged as it creeps over the weed that you cannot see it. A leaflike flatworm is similarly colored and disguised, and so are a small shrimp and a crab. Even the sargassum fish *Pterophryne*, sometimes called a "fishing frog," matches in great detail the branching fronds of the sargassum weed, including the rich brown color, golden "berries," and small white spots of tiny tubeworms. This camouflage protects the fish from enemies and also disguises it from its prey. When a small passing fish or shrimp wanders too close, *Pterophryne*'s big mouth suddenly opens and water rushes in, carrying along the intended victim. *Pterophryne* lays its eggs in a tangled nest of weed and, like all the other true sargassum-weed inhabitants, spends its entire life in this floating "island" of the tropical ocean. Other creatures visit the seaweed forest, particularly flying fish, which attach strings of sticky eggs to the weed. In the spaces between the weed their fry can safely grow.

Permanent residents of the Sargasso Sea, the sargassum fish (*right*) and the sargassum shrimp (*left*) have acquired distinctive forms of camouflage that make them inconspicuous among the masses of floating weed.

26

The great eel mystery

For centuries Europeans had wondered how it was that eels in fresh-water streams and ponds thrived and multiplied, since nobody ever saw their eggs or their young. Later on it became known that the adult eels go down to the salty sea when they are mature, never to return, and that they undergo a striking transformation before departure. The body changes from a dirty yellow to a glistening silver, and the eyes enlarge to a remarkable degree, as though the fish were preparing to go on a long, dark journey. Then nothing more is seen of the eels except for the very few that are caught by fishermen not far from the coast. But at the proper season swarms of tiny threadlike eels, called *elvers*, enter the mouths of rivers and ascend to the localities favored by their parents. As many as a million elvers have been caught in a single day as they ascended the Severn River in England. What had happened between the departure of the adults and the arrival of the young?

The first clue came near the end of the nineteenth century, when general interest in marine biology and oceanography reached a peak. This was the period when many of the still famous institutions for the study of sea life were established, first in Naples, Italy, and a little later at Plymouth, England, at Monaco, on the Mediterranean, and at Woods Hole, on Cape Cod in Massachusetts. At this time two Italian naturalists had been keeping in an aquarium some little fish known to them as *Leptocephalus brevirostris,* meaning "leaf-head short-nose." With the size, shape, and flatness of a willow leaf, this fish is as transparent as glass, except for the two black dots of its eyes, and is impossible to see in the open ocean. Simply by keeping the fish alive for sufficient time, the naturalists discovered that they transformed into common elvers.

The second clue came a few years later, when the great Danish oceanographer Johannes Schmidt caught these little fish while fishing for cod fry west of the Faeroes, a group of islands in the northeastern Atlantic. From then on he made a succession of expeditions in a westerly direction, catching specimens that were increasingly smaller the farther to the west they were caught. Finally he found the smallest in the western part of the Sargasso Sea. The adult eels apparently deposit their eggs in the sea more than a thousand feet below the surface. As the eggs develop and hatch out as minute

Glass-clear *Leptocephalus* larvae gradually transform into elvers, which ascend into fresh water and grow into the familiar eels of our rivers and streams.

Leptocephalus LARVA

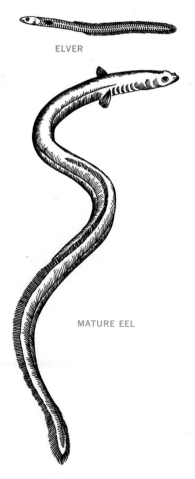

ELVER

MATURE EEL

28

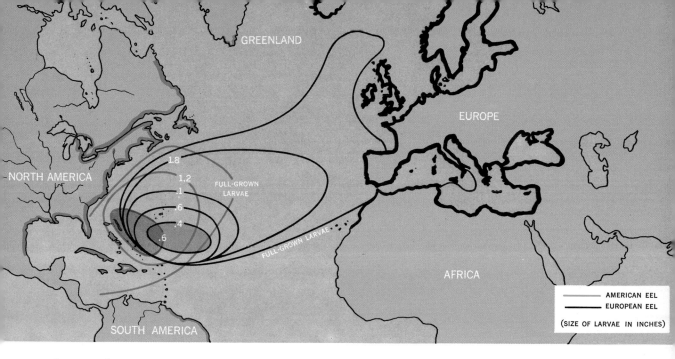

GREENLAND

EUROPE

NORTH AMERICA

1.8
1.2
1
.6
.4
FULL-GROWN LARVAE
.6
FULL-GROWN LARVAE

AFRICA

SOUTH AMERICA

——— AMERICAN EEL
——— EUROPEAN EEL
(SIZE OF LARVAE IN INCHES)

larvae, they get caught up in the moving water of the Gulf Stream swinging around the northwestern rim of the Sargasso Sea. This is the start of what is probably the longest journey ever made by helplessly drifting baby fish. The tiny larvae can swim only enough to obtain food, and so they are carried far away by the currents.

Considerable mystery remains concerning the eels, particularly with regard to their oceanic journeys and the changes that take place in the fish themselves. The eels of North America as well as Europe breed in much the same area of the Sargasso Sea, yet no one knows how the two kinds of drifting young get sorted out early in the journey so that one kind continues toward Europe and the other is taken by currents toward the North American coast. There is also the strange fact that the eel larvae that reach the American coast do so after one year, at which time they are ready to turn into elvers and ascend the rivers. Those that drift to Europe, on the other hand, take three years, whereupon they, too, change into elvers. Do the two kinds change because they are ready to do so at these very different times? Or is the change caused by their arrival in coastal waters of a different quality from the open ocean? The even greater puzzle is how the adults find their way, in this case by actually swimming, for so long a journey to such a remote spot in an enormous ocean. Obviously they must find their way or else their eggs and young would not turn up in the Sargasso Sea, but as yet no one has ever seen or caught any adult eels except at the very start of their long migration.

The life cycle of the eel poses riddles that three generations of marine biologists have not been able to answer. For example, American and European eels apparently deposit their eggs in overlapping areas in the Sargasso Sea, yet the young somehow get sorted out and always return to their ancestral shores. Also, only female eels are found in fresh water, and no one is certain about the whereabouts of the young males.

29

In typical flatfish fashion, this plaice propels itself through the water by a series of wavelike undulations of its body. It spends much of its time lying on the bottom, well concealed by its protective coloration and by a partial covering of sand that breaks up its telltale outline.

Other migrating fish

This tremendous migration of old and new generations of eels using the great current systems of the ocean is an extreme example of the sort of migration a great many other fish carry out on a smaller scale. Usually such migrations are necessary when young fish are so small that they are carried helplessly along in a current. If parent fish simply shed their small eggs where they feed, currents would carry the eggs and helpless young to places where they could not survive. What the fish do about this is seen in the plaice, a flounder-like fish common in the North Sea and an important food fish that has been closely studied.

Plaice are bottom-dwelling flatfish found in many areas of shallow sea off Britain and Europe, especially off the coast of Holland, where they find abundant food on the sandy

30

sea floor. If the adult fish were to shed their eggs in this region, however, the currents would carry them far away from the best feeding grounds. The plaice migrate against the current to a place about midway between the coast of Holland and the coast of England, where the water is somewhat deeper. It is estimated that about sixty million plaice assemble to spawn there in midwinter. The young fish that hatch from the eggs feed and grow for about a month in the surface layer of the sea. During that time they drift back with the current toward the feeding ground their parents had left when they started their spawning migration. At the end of a month, when the current has brought them over the feeding ground, the young fish change into small fish more like their parents and descend to the sea floor to live. The fish make use of the currents so that at each stage of their lives, from egg to adult, they are in the right place at the right time. This, of course, is a rule of survival for all living things. Timing is most important.

Another way of stating this rule is that the fish must be in the proper condition to do what they have to do in a particular place. For example, the adult plaice assembling in the breeding area for spawning must be fully mature and ready to spawn, or else their migration to this area would be a wasted effort. Plaice and other flatfish, moreover, are remarkable in that they lie on the sea floor on one side. Both eyes are on either the right or the left side of the head, whichever side is uppermost. When the young fish hatch from the eggs, however, and throughout their journey in the upper layer of the sea, they swim upright like other fish and have one eye on each side of the head. When the time comes to sink to the sea floor, one eye gradually shifts across the nose to the other side (to the right side in sole, plaice, and flounder, and to the left in brill and turbot), and the metamorphosed, or changed, fish are ready to start a very different sort of existence lasting for the rest of their lives.

Ocean currents force fish to make migrations, and the fish have met the challenge more strikingly than most other creatures of the sea. Flatfish make short migrations, mainly, no doubt, because there is no need for longer journeys. Also their body shape and habits make fast, long-distance travel difficult. Most of the fish that cope with the wider ocean are more powerful and more streamlined. You might wonder how these fish manage to find their way on these longer journeys far away from shore and far above the sea floor.

All flatfish start out life as conventional upright swimmers, but soon they begin to lean to one side. By the time they are an inch or so long, they swim in a fully horizontal position and are ready for bottom dwelling. This transformation is accompanied by the migration of the "bottom" eye over or even through the head, to join the "top" eye on what becomes the fish's upper surface.

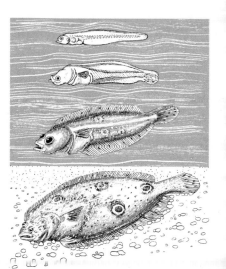

MASTERS OF
CAMOUFLAGE

Most people think of chameleons as the color-change specialists of the animal kingdom, but the flatfish are the real champions. Look at—or look for—the flounder shown here on two different bottom surfaces. Besides matching the background's color to near perfection, the fish also captures with remarkable fidelity the effect of the texture—fine sand in the left-hand photograph, coarse gravel and pebbles in the right-hand photograph.

These marvelous powers of disguise are due to special pigment-bearing cells called *chromatophores*, located in the skin tissue just under the fish's transparent scales. The pigment may be yellow, orange, red, or black. The chromatophore can be expanded

or contracted, so that more or less of the pigment is visible. The skin also contains bodies called *iridocytes,* which reflect light like tiny mirrors and can affect the fish's coloration in two ways. First, depending on how deeply they are buried in the skin, they produce the chalky whites and metallic silvers common among fishes. Second, the iridocytes optically interact with the chromatophores to produce colors not available from the chromatophore pigments—blue and green, for example. Selective expansion and contraction of chromatophores throughout the skin allow the flounder to produce an almost unlimited variety of camouflage patterns, such as the two shown here.

From salt water to fresh

Eels travel about three thousand miles from Europe and one thousand miles from the American coast to their meeting place in the tropical ocean. Other fish may travel similar distances, though we know little about them. The Pacific salmon, for instance, which spends the early part of its life in fresh-water streams, enters the sea to complete its growth as a truly oceanic feeder and wanderer. But it finally returns to the particular small stream of its infancy to reproduce and immediately die. All that we know of this amazing ability of the adult salmon is that the fish recognizes its birthplace by actually smelling and tasting the water through which it journeys. Does it find its way through enormous distances in the ocean by these chemical senses alone, or by other senses as well? No one knows, but we do know that ocean currents are pathways that fish may well be able to follow. In fact, fish are so sensitive to the chemistry and the physical conditions (such as temperature and density) of the water in which they swim that they may find it hard to stray outside certain natural boundaries.

One reason ocean currents can serve as a guide to migrating fish is that the currents do not mix. As an extreme example, consider the area where a large river runs out to sea. It is an extreme example because river water has very little salt and ocean water has a great deal. Fresh water floats on top of salty seawater unless forcibly mixed. Accordingly, when a river such as the Amazon or the Mississippi runs out to sea, the surface water is fresh or brackish for as much as a hundred miles from land. If the river is deep where it joins the sea, a tongue of ocean water may extend up the riverbed for many miles, with the river water flowing over it. Then you may see fishermen actually fishing down through the fresh water for sea fish, such as cod, in the salt water below.

Silt-laden fresh water from the Colorado River flows far out into the Gulf of California before mixing with the ocean's salt water. The ever-increasing saltiness of the ocean is due largely to substances carried into it by the world's rivers. The Colorado River alone annually adds some fourteen million tons of dissolved mineral salts to the ocean. (This unusual photograph was taken at an altitude of 140 miles by astronauts James A. McDivitt and Edward H. White on the flight of *Gemini IV*.)

A ribbon of life

In much the same way, chances are very slight that ocean currents flowing side by side will mix together, particularly when there are differences in the density of the water resulting from variations in salt content or in temperature, or when there are differences in speed. The marine naturalist William Beebe saw an exceptional example of this in 1926, on his voyage aboard the research vessel *Arcturus*. The ship was cruising westward in the Pacific Ocean close to the equator, several hundred miles from the coast of Central America, when he saw a line in the water stretching from horizon to horizon. On the south side of the line the sea was dark and rough. To the north it was much lighter and smoother. When the ship reached the line, it turned out to be a band of foam only about sixty feet wide. Whitecaps marked the shared edges of two great ocean currents, both flowing west. The line zigzagged across the sea as far as the eye could see. The water in both currents was warm, but the southern current was several degrees colder than the northern and flowed considerably faster. These differences extended downward for at least two thousand feet. The *Arcturus* followed this current *rip*,

A "gam," or school, of dolphins may follow for miles along the thin boundary line between two masses of water, feasting on the abundance of ocean life concentrated there by the current rip.

as such boundaries of currents are called, for more than a hundred miles. The sharp line between the two massive currents on either side of the rip could be as good a guide for fish traveling through the ocean as a ditch alongside a path might be for a man walking through a forest at night.

The abundance of life along the current rip amazed the naturalists aboard the ship. It was as though all the life of the ocean had congregated just there. Yet ten yards from the line on either side the water appeared empty of life. The most obvious creatures in sight were the sea birds: tropic-birds, boobies, frigatebirds, and hundreds of phalaropes.

In the water Beebe and his companions saw at one time five to six hundred dolphins, which are actually small whales somewhat larger than a man. They were leaping and feeding as they followed the line, attracted by the tens of thousands of young fish called amber jacks.

All about was a thick soup of small, delicate soft-bodied creatures on which the amber jacks were feeding. These included beautiful and colorful floating sea anemones; the purple-shelled *Ianthina* snail, which lives only on the ocean surface; the deep-blue tufted sea slug called *Glaucus*; the

Three carnivorous pelagic mollusks called *Glaucus* prey on a *Porpita,* a close relative of the Portuguese man-of-war. The inch-long *Glaucus* is undaunted by the *Porpita's* stinging cells. Moreover, through some unknown process it actually absorbs these cells, undischarged and still potent, into its body and uses them for its own defense. *Glaucus* has also evolved an interesting solution to the flotation problem: it spends its life floating upside down, clinging to the underside of the surface film of the water.

The tentacles of a sailor-by-the-wind provide a meal for an *Ianthina*, a remarkable sea snail that is able to live on the surface by means of a paper-thin shell and a raft of tough bubbles, both clearly shown here. Particularly partial to sailors-by-the-wind, *Ianthina* may anesthetize its victims so that their tentacles stay uncontracted while it dines at its leisure.

blue and gold *Porpita,* which are floating disks closely related to the sailors-by-the-wind, or *Velella,* although without a sail; and hosts of many other animals as well as buoyant eggs. The *Ianthina* snails keep themselves afloat by means of a bubble raft made of slime and air, and their purple color appears to be the result of browsing on the blue-purple *Porpita* and *Velella.* And following along with it all, in addition to air-breathing sea turtles, sea birds, and true dolphins, were fast-swimming dolphin fish and several kinds of open-ocean sharks.

Many logs went drifting by, covered with barnacles because they had been in the sea so long. There were palm, coconut, bamboo, and trumpetwood trunks carried out to sea by mainland rivers and swept away by the current. Many were tunneled through and through by shipworm, the long

This log has been opened up to show you shipworm damage; on the outer surface you might find only inconspicuous pinholes where the creatures made their entry as tiny larvae. Not a worm at all, the shipworm is a clam whose shell has been adapted into an efficient rasping tool for cutting quarter-inch tunnels through wood.

pencil-shaped clam *Teredo*, which penetrates all floating wood in tropical seas; it has riddled the hulls of sailing ships since men first began to sail and caused Columbus himself to lose a ship on his second voyage to the Caribbean. The floating logs were also the homes of many creatures besides *Teredo*. Multitudes of normally shore-living crabs of many kinds and colors, some carrying masses of developing eggs, crept in and out of the crevices and cracks; all were taking a free ride to somewhere or nowhere, far across the ocean.

How currents are formed

In addition to countless species of animals, Beebe saw thirty-eight kinds of trees, plants, and seeds traveling with the current rip in a generally westerly direction. Everything that could float on, or close to, the surface of the sea seemed to have been gathered into this narrow band of water. But why was everything concentrated in this ribbon of foamy water? Why was the ocean on either side so empty of life, and where could such a current take its load of living things?

The first two questions can be answered as one. Ocean currents, like currents of air in the atmosphere, move from place to place in a more complicated way than you might suppose. The column of water or of air, as the case may be, not only travels in a particular direction but spirals as it goes, with a corkscrewlike twist. Furthermore, when two currents are flowing along side by side, they usually spiral in opposite directions, clockwise in one and counterclockwise in the other. This motion establishes the rip where the edges of the two currents touch. At the particular rip Beebe studied, surface water not only traveled westward but moved toward the line from each side and there turned downward to a considerable depth. All the floating objects at the surface, whether alive or not, were carried toward the line where the currents came together; they remained floating at the surface in the rip and traveled with it. In this way the currents were sweeping most of the nearby ocean surface bare and gathering everything together in the rip.

41

Drifters from the shore

A current in the ocean can carry land or shore life from one territory to another. In the Atlantic Ocean, for instance, it is possible that debris carried out to sea by African rivers such as the Congo and the Niger can travel across the ocean in the Equatorial Current, to be cast up on the shores of Brazil or the Caribbean. Probably many of the ancestors of the unique and spectacular animal and plant life of the Galápagos Islands originally reached there by means of the

Some distant ancestor of this Galapagos iguana was carried from the mainland as an involuntary voyager, perhaps aboard a current-borne dead tree. The masked booby, although free to come and go, is attracted to the islands by the abundance of fish fostered by the same currents. Thus the wind-driven ocean currents influence the life of the land and the air as well as that of the sea.

Equatorial Current in the Pacific Ocean. The islands themselves are some five hundred miles off the coast of Ecuador.
The current rip we have described would have carried its
living freight on a course not far from those islands, and at
some time in the distant past lizards and land turtles must
have ridden unwillingly on logs and other rafts of vegetation, across the tropical ocean from somewhere in South
America. Altogether the wind-blown currents of the open
ocean are pathways for life of many kinds.

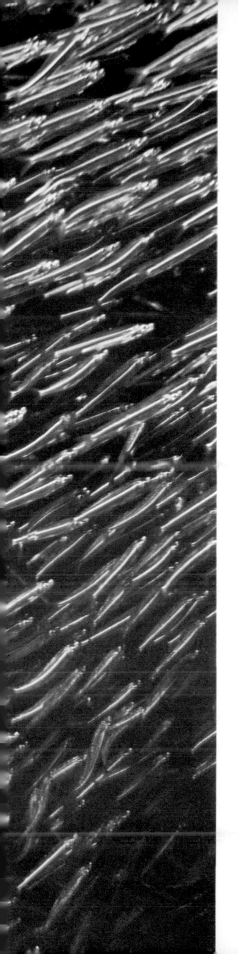

Below the
Ocean's Surface

Even if you have seen a current rip and its remarkable variety of living contents, you have observed only a tiny fraction of the many living species in the ocean. Most of the ocean's life lies away from the shore, almost entirely below the surface but far above the floor. Some of it you can see where the tide sweeps close to rocks. You can see more if you row out from shore in a boat and look down where the sea is calm. In spring and summer, jellyfish go drifting by, often as far down as the eye can see. The water itself will usually be somewhat greenish with uncountable numbers of microscopic plants.

Along with the plants, all sorts of animal life abound in this uppermost layer of the ocean. Off the coast, out to the edge of the continental shelf, the sea is not very deep and light reaches to the sea floor itself. Farther out, the bottom drops off steeply to the deep sea, and only dark, cold ocean water underlies the sunlit upper layer. There the ocean floor may be miles below the surface. Yet all around the world, the upper portion of every ocean is part of one continuous layer of light and life. What lies almost at your feet when you look down into the sea from the end of a wharf is part of the same rich layer that floats above the deepest sea and reaches the farthest corners of the globe.

Plant life everywhere, on land or in the sea, requires light, water, and mineral salts to grow. The sea usually offers all these, though the amounts of light and of certain minerals vary from season to season. Both on land and in the sea, plants have to contend with the force of gravity. On land most plants have woody stems that support them above the ground and roots that hold them in place. In the sea the surrounding water supports the plants, just as it does the body of a fish or a human being, although not entirely. Large bodies, whether plant or animal, usually sink slowly toward the sea floor unless they are buoyed up by gas chambers, such as those in sargassum weed and bony fish. The upper layer of the ocean therefore supplies everything a plant requires except complete support, and most seaweeds live only along the fringe of the ocean where they can hang on to rocks and so remain in shallow, well-lighted water.

Where the water is deeper and there is nothing to cling to, ocean plants are microscopic. Minute particles in water, like dust particles in the air, either do not sink at all or sink so slowly that any movement of the water or air keeps them from settling. The lesser tendency of minute organisms, whether plants or animals, to sink is the result of *viscosity*, or stickiness, a property of water and other liquids. Water is viscous, but less so than syrup. It clings to some extent to everything that lives in the sea. This stickiness, or drag, slows down the rate at which any object may sink. An object with a relatively large outside surface in contact with water sinks more slowly than one of equal weight but a smaller surface. A thousand separate microscopic one-celled plants or animals have hundreds of times more exposed surface than a thousand cells making up a single organism of the same weight. As separate cells they would sink several hundred times more slowly than they would if they were together in a single compact mass.

Plants that wander

Even though you cannot see the smallest oceanic plants with your naked eye, and even though they consist mostly of separate single cells, they are so numerous that together they just about equal the amount of all the vegetation on land.

Ascophyllum, sometimes called knotted wrack, is a common seaweed along rocky shores. The gas-filled bladders along the strands hold the plant upright in the water. *Ascophyllum* is exposed to the air at low tide, and the bladders burst with a popping noise if you step on them.

46

They are the pasture of the sea, for all animal life depends on them for food either directly or indirectly. Because they drift wherever the ocean currents take them, they are known as the *phytoplankton*, which means "plants that wander." You can collect them by towing behind a boat a conical net of nylon with a collecting jar tied in the end. Go very slowly, no faster than you can row. Among the most abundant of the microscopic plants are the diatoms, and wherever the sea has a somewhat greenish or yellowish tinge you can be sure that diatoms will be plentiful.

To examine diatoms, you must look at them under a microscope—a high-powered microscope, if possible, for they are very small. Each cell is enclosed by a glasslike external wall. The protective shell is composed of two halves, two lidlike structures that fit into one another to enclose the body in a little box: hence the name *diatom*, meaning "cut in two."

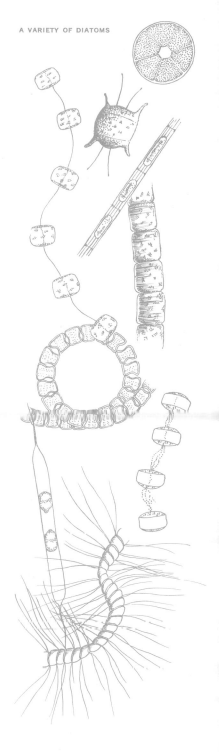

Manufacturing with light

Like all other green plants each diatom is a small factory that manufactures living substances. Sunlight supplies the energy to power the factory, and the water contains the simple raw materials. Inside each diatom, many brown-green disks, or *chloroplasts*, absorb light and carry on the manufacturing process known as *photosynthesis*, "building with light." Innumerable small holes in the glasslike box allow the inner living substance to come into actual contact with the ocean water. The holes also make the wall lighter. Furthermore this breaking up of the wall into a complex pattern of openings, ridges, dents, and other fine structures greatly increases the extent of the whole outside surface. Many diatoms are drawn out like needles or are flattened, twisted, or supplied with long hairlike structures that increase their surface area without increasing their weight. Thus diatoms float in the water much as a feather or a dandelion seed floats in the air because its surface is so great in relation to its weight. In warm seas, where the water is actually less dense than in cold seas, the tendency to sink is greater, and so both microscopic plants and the nearly microscopic crustaceans often have extraordinary extensions of their bodies to aid them in keeping afloat. (Try floating in water with your arms out and with them against your sides. Which way do you float more easily?)

47

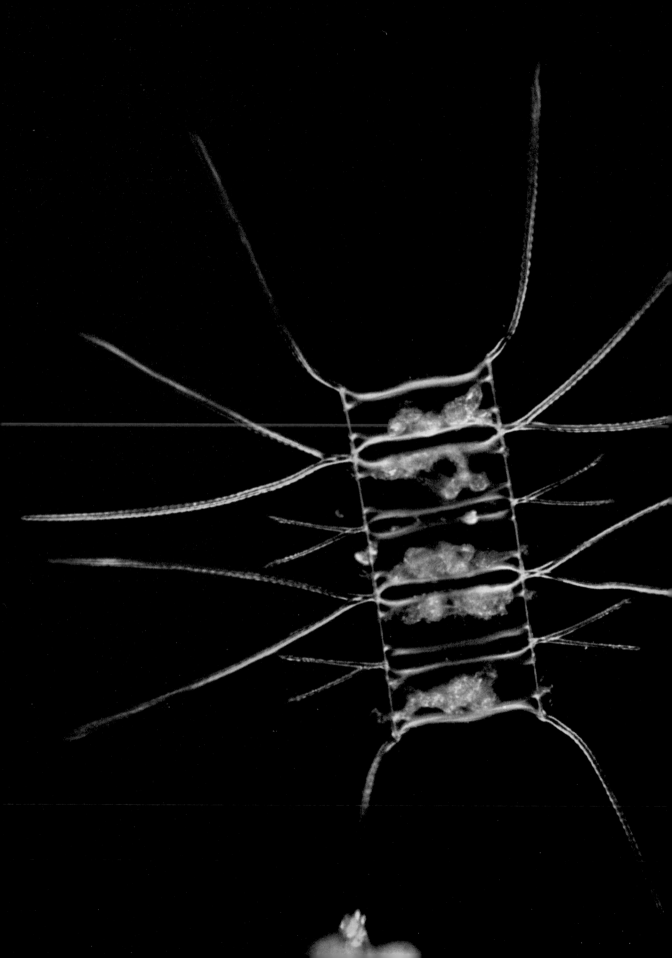

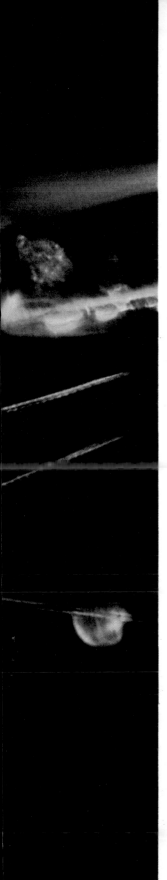

DIATOMS—OCEAN "GRASS"

As the most important foodstuff in the sea, diatoms are comparable to the grasses of dry land. They may occur as single individuals, such as *Rhizosolenia* (*right,* magnified 270 times), or as linked chains of varying lengths, like these five *Chaetoceros* diatoms (*left,* magnified 1600 times). In either case, each cell is a complete, independent green plant, a miniature chemical factory that uses solar energy to convert inorganic substances into the materials vital to animal life—carbohydrates, fats, proteins, vitamins. Virtually all ocean animals, from crustaceans to whales, depend directly or indirectly upon the microscopic diatoms for sustenance, just as land animals (including man) are ultimately dependent upon grasses and other plants.

Like all green plants, diatoms can flourish only in the presence of light, and various flotation devices keep them in the upper layers of the water. *Rhizosolenia*'s long, thin shape and *Chaetoceros*'s four hairlike shell extensions slow their sinking.

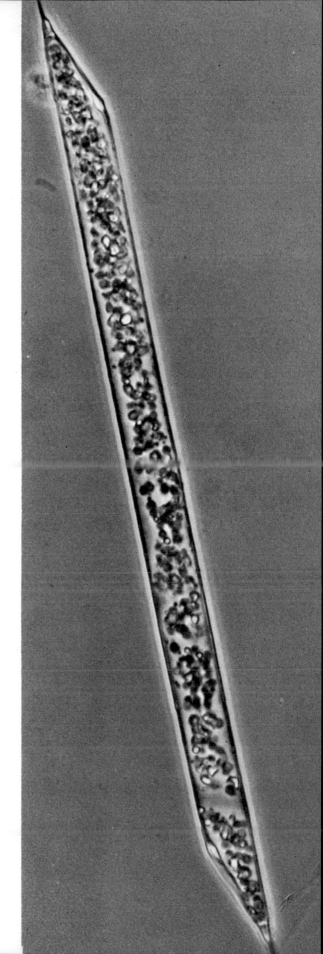

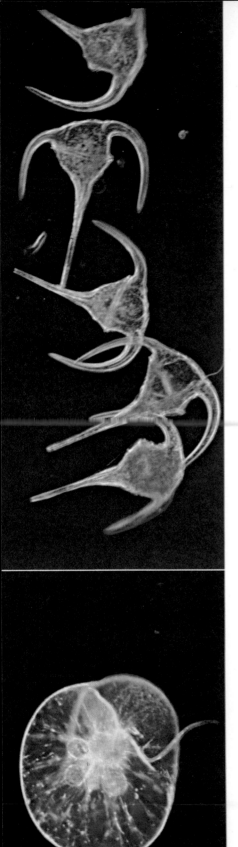

Living light

If you go down to the sea on a dark spring or summer night and throw a stone in the water, the chances are that the splash will sparkle brightly in spite of the darkness. You may also see a sparkling wake in the water behind the sinking stone, like the tail of a comet. This is living light, called *bioluminescence*, produced by thousands of microscopic organisms, but not by diatoms.

Charles Darwin described bioluminescence during the voyage of the *Beagle*, more than a century ago:

> While sailing a little south of the Plata on one very dark night the sea presented a wonderful and most beautiful spectacle. There was a fresh breeze, and every part of the surface which during the day is seen as foam, now glowed with a pale light. The vessel drove before her bows two billows of liquid phosphorus, and in her wake she was followed by a milky train. As far as the eye reached, the crest of every wave was bright.

The microscopic organisms responsible for the display are single cells known as *dinoflagellates*, or armored flagellates, so called because they all have a slender whiplike flagellum with which they propel themselves through the water. Most of them have a protective outer case made of a horny substance rather than the glasslike silicon enclosing diatoms. Each dinoflagellate possesses a small eyespot that is sensitive to light. The eyespot and the flagellum work together so that the organism moves in the direction from which light comes, in this case the surface of the sea. Most of these armored flagellates, which are usually brown or green (although some are red), possess chlorophyll and manufacture living substances in the same way as diatoms and other plants. Like the diatoms they are swept along with the ocean currents, but their flagella enable them to keep from sinking by continually moving upward, at least during the hours of daylight. In addition, many of them have long projecting spines that

Plants or animals? The dinoflagellate group includes both. *Ceratium* (*above*, magnified forty-three times) manufactures its food through photosynthesis, but *Noctiluca* (*below*, magnified thirty times) preys on diatoms and other small organisms.

50

counteract the tendency to sink. Like diatoms, they may be so abundant that they color the water for miles at a stretch. They are particularly plentiful in the warmer regions, whereas diatoms are most abundant in colder oceans.

One of the brightest and largest of the luminescent flagellates is *Noctiluca*, a name that means "night light." It is very common in the cooler seas, especially in late summer and autumn. Then the bow wave and the wake of a boat will shine like silver fire from the phosphorescence of millions of *Noctiluca*. The light is so brilliant that in the darkest night it is often possible to read a newspaper by it. About the size of a pinhead, just large enough to be seen with the naked eye, *Noctiluca* is mostly a gelatinous substance that is lighter than water. Although it drifts like a balloon and cannot direct its own movements, this flagellate differs from most of its kind in being more animallike than plantlike, for it lacks chlorophyll. Instead of utilizing sunlight for building up its own substance, it feeds on other living organisms smaller than itself. Its flagellum has become an organ for seizing prey, primarily diatoms. Increase in size and the consequent evolution of flagella have made possible the change from the role of producer to that of predator, from producing living substance from nonliving raw materials to consuming living matter.

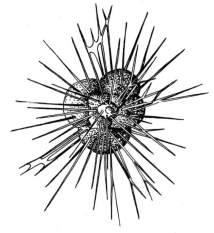

FORAMINIFERAN (*Globigerina*)

One-celled fishermen

Because it eats plants, *Noctiluca* is a member of the animal plankton, or zooplankton, a host of minute forms of animal life. Another creature not unlike *Noctiluca* in size and habits, although not luminescent, is *Globigerina*. It is one of the most abundant organisms in northern oceans, important both as a predator and as a source of food for creatures of somewhat larger size. Each individual consists of two or three spherical limy, or *calcareous*, shells bearing numerous spines that aid in keeping it afloat. Each shell is perforated all over to permit threads of living substances to protrude and form an external network. This network traps diatoms and other smaller organisms, which are digested outside the shell and then absorbed within. Such an arrangement is typical not only of *Globigerina* but of all the Foraminifera, the group to which it belongs. *Globigerina* and its relatives and one other group, the beautiful Radiolaria, seem to be as large as one-celled

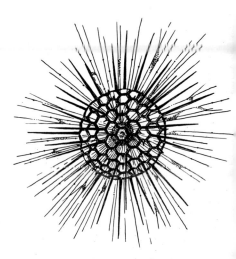

RADIOLARIAN (*Heliosphaera*)

The foraminiferans and the radiolarians are both one-celled organisms, and both have evolved similar solutions to the flotation problem—many-spined shells that drag against the water's viscosity. But one difference is as striking as this similarity: the foraminiferans build shells of calcium; the radiolarians, of silica.

51

animals can become. They are large enough to feed on diatoms and, in fact, on any planktonic plants and animals smaller than themselves. But they are unable to move about and are kept afloat mainly by the numerous long spines of lime or silica that project into the surrounding water.

Already we can see the general circumstances of life in the upper layer of the ocean. The smallest and most abundant kinds are microscopic plants that can grow and survive only where light can reach them. They are so small that they easily stay afloat. Such plants are an almost inexhaustible source of food for any animallike organisms able to capture and digest them, but these predators must be considerably larger than their prey. When we look at the other creatures of the animal plankton, we see that as they become larger they can feed on a greater variety of organisms, but only by expending a great deal of energy capturing prey and staying afloat.

Ocean food chains

Apart from the enormous numbers of diatoms, flagellates, and other truly productive organisms that manufacture living substance from water and light, the most vital link in the ocean's chain of life consists of those creatures that feed directly upon them. Not many animals are able to do so, since the producers are individually so small. A large marine animal, whether fish or jellyfish, trying to feed directly on diatoms would not be able to swallow enough water to obtain sufficient food. An important rule with few exceptions seems to be that each kind of creature feeds on something smaller than itself, but not too much smaller. And each be-

comes the food of something larger than itself, but not too much larger. This gradual stepping up constitutes a food chain.

The most successful diatom feeders are very small crustaceans known as *copepods*, most of which are just large enough to be seen. One kind, called *Calanus*, is about a quarter of an inch long. It is one of the most important animals in the ocean, and several marine research vessels have been named for it.

This small animal and its closest relatives are the grazers of the diatom sea pasture. Although they can make strong swimming movements with their six pairs of limbs, most of the time they tread water, so to speak. Meanwhile they keep the fanlike appendages around their mouths moving with astonishing rapidity, up to sixty strokes per second. In this way they float at a fixed level in the water and at the same time draw water toward themselves in a sort of small whirlpool. The water passes through extremely fine sieves to screen out diatoms and other minute plants and even bacteria. When enough have accumulated, other appendages push the food into the mouths.

The copepods of the *Calanus* type are thus extremely efficient collectors of the phytoplankton. And they are so abundant that they form the principal food of herring, the most plentiful fish in the ocean. Herring fishermen call the *Calanus* "red feed" because of its pink color. At times *Calanus* are so numerous that the ocean water itself seems to take on the color. In the Gulf of Maine it took one marine biologist only about fifteen minutes to catch more than two and a half million *Calanus* in a conical net just one yard in diameter. Where the *Calanus* are, the herring are almost sure to follow, and the herring in turn serve as food for a multi-

Every creature in the ocean is a member of a food chain, in which each "link" feeds upon the one below it and is fed upon by the one above it. Here is a simple four-link food chain. Diatoms are consumed by the small *Calanus* crustaceans, which are preyed upon by herring, which in turn are preyed upon by tuna. But the chain does not end here, for even more predacious animals feed upon the tuna—not the least of them, man.

tude of larger creatures such as tuna, squid, porpoises, and man himself. Here, then, is a complete food chain: diatom to copepod to small fish to larger creatures of one kind or another.

The herring's changing diet

Although many kinds of marine animals spend all of their life in the upper layer of the ocean, either as part of the plankton or as swimming creatures that feed on plankton, many other kinds spend only the early part of their life in this region. Even the herring does not spend its entire existence swimming in the upper layer of the ocean. Herring lay their eggs in sticky masses attached to stones on the sea floor, each herring laying at least ten thousand eggs. The eggs are thus anchored while the embryos develop, and consequently the young are not carried away by ocean currents until they have hatched. In this way there is some assurance that they will be in the right place to feed when they do start life on their own. On the other hand, a penalty is paid,

HERRING FEEDING HABITS

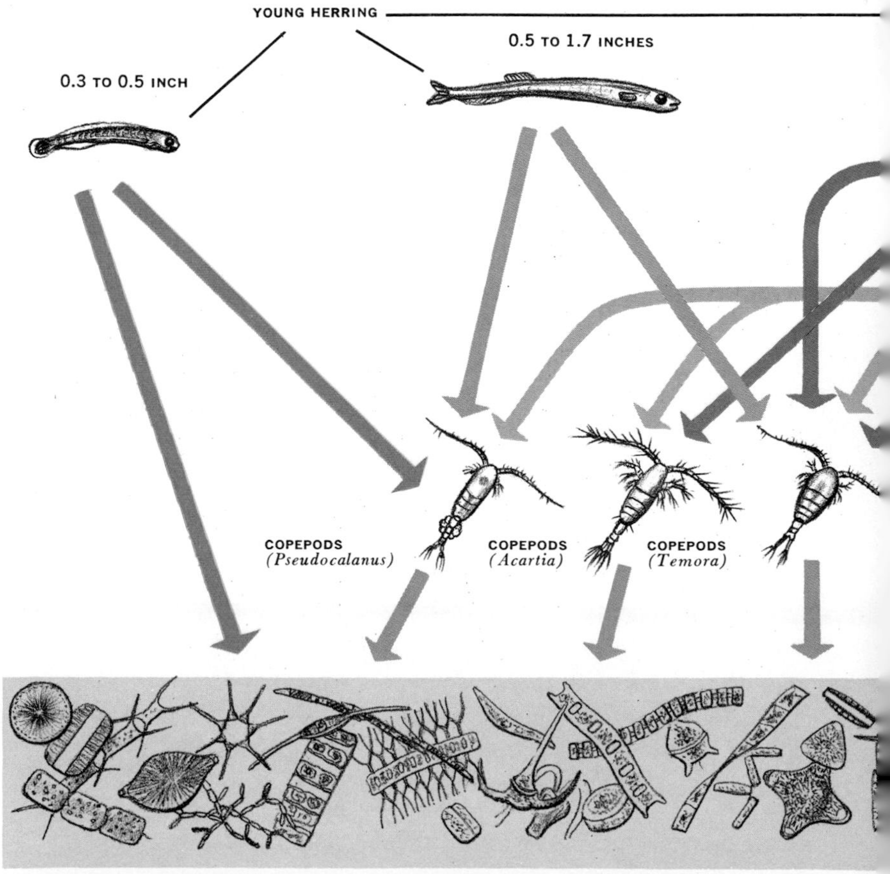

YOUNG HERRING

0.5 TO 1.7 INCHES

0.3 TO 0.5 INCH

An animal's position in a food chain frequently changes as it grows older. The herring, for example, starts out life by feeding directly upon the diatoms and dinoflagellates of the phytoplankton. Soon the fish is large enough to feed upon the next higher link in the chain, the small copepods. As it continues to grow, its diet shifts to progressively larger crustaceans. Finally, as an adult, it preys upon many of the largest members of the plankton community.

COPEPODS
(*Pseudocalanus*)

COPEPODS
(*Acartia*)

COPEPODS
(*Temora*)

because the egg masses are eaten in large quantities by bottom-feeding fish such as haddock.

Herring that hatch swim up to the surface waters and feed on diatoms. They are already equipped with strainers for sifting water, which consist of gill rakers, processes extending from the sides of their gills. These form a grid that permits the water taken in through the mouth to flow out through the gills, as in all fish. But the rakers prevent the diatoms from escaping, so that they pass down to the stomach. The herring fry, however, grow larger, and so does the size of the gill-raker mesh in the gills. Diatoms escape with the water, but now, with the greater intake of water, copepods flow in and are retained because they are bigger than the mesh. In this case the fish uses the same feeding apparatus throughout its life, but as the fish gets larger it catches a different crop.

In contrast to the herring, mackerel and other fish shed their eggs freely in the water to develop while drifting with the currents. These hatch into small fry equipped with the same sort of gill raker sieves as those of young herring, but large enough to catch copepods rather than diatoms.

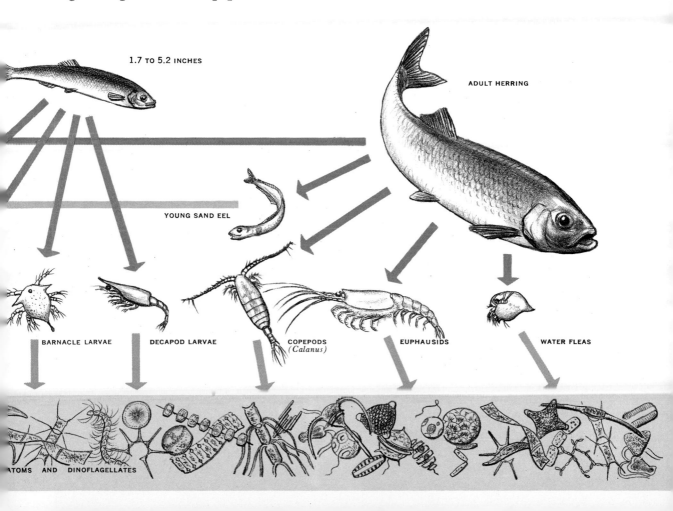

1.7 TO 5.2 INCHES

ADULT HERRING

YOUNG SAND EEL

BARNACLE LARVAE   DECAPOD LARVAE   COPEPODS (Calanus)   EUPHAUSIDS   WATER FLEAS

ATOMS AND DINOFLAGELLATES

The swimming larvae

The great majority of sea-floor creatures, such as starfish, sea urchins, snails, clams, worms, crabs, lobsters, and many others, produce young that spend the first stages of their active life swimming and feeding as part of the oceanic plankton. The food supply of the diatom sea pasture is extremely rich, at least at certain times of the year, and is uniquely suitable as food for minute larvae.

The larger such larvae can grow before they sink down to the sea floor to live, the more likely they are to survive when they arrive on the bottom. A problem therefore arises. The more such larvae succeed in growing, the heavier they become and the more inclined they are to sink. Consequently, we see a great many devices that enable these growing larvae to stay afloat longer than would otherwise be possible. The kinds of larvae in the plankton vary with the species, the numbers, and the breeding seasons of the animals that live on the sea floor below.

All crustaceans, including crabs and lobsters, carry their eggs until the larvae hatch. Then the larvae swim up toward the light to become part of the plankton community. If the eggs are very small, the young that hatch are known as *nauplius larvae*. These have a single eye in the middle of the

A single female crab may produce as many as two million eggs, each hatching a zoea larva like this one (*above*, magnified twenty-six times). The zoea swims upward to the surface waters to feed—and be fed upon—as a member of the plankton community. After a period of growth, during which it casts its skin several times, the zoea abruptly transforms into a megalops (*right*, magnified twenty-three times). The megalops soon becomes too heavy for planktonic life, and so it tucks its tail under and sinks to the ocean floor, where it becomes an adult crab.

head, three pairs of swimming appendages, and a forked tail. Nauplius larvae are the first stage in the life of copepods and barnacles; and in the season when the barnacle larvae are common in the plankton, they serve as an important source of food for water-straining fish.

Crabs, on the other hand, have larger eggs, and the young that hatch are more advanced, though very different in appearance from their parents. Crabs hatch as *zoea larvae*, each with a pair of well-developed eyes, three pairs of swimming appendages, a forked tail, and long spines extending from the region of the head to aid it in keeping afloat. As they grow, they cast their skins periodically, as do all growing crustaceans. Suddenly they change into a final swimming stage, called the *megalops*, in which they look more like a crab but have extended tails. They are only a fraction of an inch long, but they are as large as they can grow and still remain swimming in the ocean. Shortly, they sink to the sea floor, tuck their tails beneath their bodies, and continue their lives as typical sea-floor crabs.

The common lobster has a similar life history, although its swimming larvae do not have distinctive names. In fact, they look a good deal like lobsters from the start, except that they have relatively long and slender bodies and better swimming appendages. After growing to a length of about a third of an inch, they too sink to the sea floor, unable to stay afloat any longer. The southern lobster, or crawfish, which has no large claws, grows to a much larger size as a member of the plankton. The larva, called *phyllosoma*, is flat like a leaf and has extremely long, thin appendages, including eyestalks. Even though it thus has a relatively large surface area, the time comes when gravity wins. After another casting of the skin the creature, looking much more like its parent, sinks to the sea floor, where it will spend the remainder of its existence.

The larvae of some animals have tiny hairs which keep them afloat. Starfish larvae swim by means of these microscopic, rhythmically beating living hairs known as *cilia*. The larvae of sea urchins, relatives of the starfish, are generally similar to starfish larvae but in addition have long, straight arms also covered with beating cilia; these are most effective in keeping the organism afloat. And, as a last example of this sort of device employed by larvae to stay afloat, there are the *veliger larvae* of marine snails. The veliger looks

Many marine snails that are bottom dwellers as adults begin life as planktonic veliger larvae, like the one shown here, magnified twenty times. The four paddlelike body extensions are lined with active cilia, which help the larva to stay afloat and enable it to swim through the water.

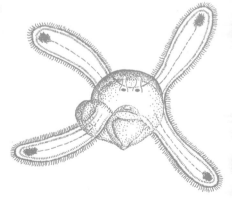

like a miniature snail, but its front end is enormously expanded into a kind of figure-eight structure, equipped with long and powerful cilia. The action of the cilia pulls the creature along through the water as if it were equipped with a propeller.

The larvae of these creatures, together with crustacean larvae, feed continuously on the diatoms and other microscopic life of the plankton until they grow so heavy that they sink to the sea floor to stay. In the meantime they constitute an important part of the ocean community, both as consumers of phytoplankton and as food for other creatures.

Transparent predators

Like a trout on a fisherman's hook, a two-inch fish vainly struggles to escape the numbing, sticky grip of a jellyfish tentacle. The jellyfish shown here is *Dactylometra*, commonly called the sea nettle because of the burning, itching sting it delivers to the swimmer unlucky enough to brush up against it.

Some of the commonest creatures inhabiting the upper waters and feeding on copepods, larvae, and young fish are nearly invisible, not because they are small but because they are practically transparent. They have an extremely high proportion of water in their body tissues, usually in the form of jelly. Jellyfish may consist of as much as ninety-six percent water, leaving very little matter for making up the shape and substance of the living creature. Thus in addition to being transparent and therefore invisible to the small creatures

it preys upon, the animal is hardly heavier than the surrounding water and so has a minimum of work to do to stay in place. You may look down into the ocean from a boat and see nothing, even though the water is teeming with life of many kinds. But often enough, you will see color, particularly in the tropics, adding to the beauty of these jelly-like organisms. It was easier to see them in the past, from the decks of sailing ships, than now from the high decks of the ocean liners. Perhaps the first Englishman to write about them was Richard Hawkins, an Elizabethan sea captain, who had this to say of the things he saw in the ocean while waiting to intercept treasure-laden ships returning to Spain from America:

I saw in 1590, lying with a fleet of her majesties ships about the islands of the Azores, almost six months, the greatest part of the time we were becalmed, all the sea so replenished with several sorts of jellies, and forms of serpents, adders, snakes as seemed wonderful; some green, some black, some yellow, some white, some of diverse colors; and many of them had life, and some there were a yard and a half, and two yards long; which had I not seen, I could hardly have believed. A man could not draw a bucket of water clear of some such life.

By now paralyzed or dead, the fish is drawn up into the sea nettle's stomach. *Dactylometra* commonly attains a size of four to eight inches across, although a few individuals may reach a foot in width.

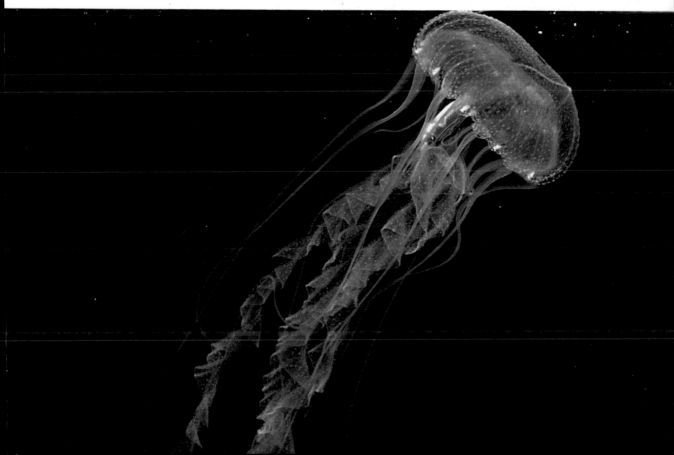

While following the current rip in the Pacific Ocean, William Beebe had a similar experience. Every bucket dipped in the sea came up full of gelatinous inhabitants of the upper ocean, although they were apparently of a less colorful sort than those seen by Hawkins more than three centuries before. Creatures such as these are rarely studied alive because they are so fragile and break up when caught in nets. But to those who have seen them, either in the sea or in aquariums, they are among the most fascinating of all life of the ocean.

Arrowworms and comb jellies

One of the most invisible predators is the glass-clear arrowworm, about an inch long. It is actually not a worm at all, but a truly oceanic creature with no known relatives. Most of the time it stays motionless, although drifting with the currents, and moves only when some unsuspecting copepod or fish larva comes too close to its tiny jaws. Yet arrowworms are so numerous that they themselves are captured in quantity by water-straining fish such as herring and serve as an important source of food.

Other equally transparent inhabitants of the currents sweeping across the open ocean are the comb jellies, which are even more jellylike than jellyfish. Sea gooseberry is one of their common names. Each swims by means of eight rows of continually beating combs of cilia, trailing a pair of long tentacles to capture prey. Even when you examine some in a vessel of water, usually all you can see is the iridescent light reflected by the beating combs. Some comb jellies, however, are shaped more like cucumbers. The most spectacular kind, called the "girdle of Venus," is undoubtedly one of those that Hawkins saw, for it is drawn out to the dimensions of a belt. This is a rarer sort, but the more usual kinds of comb jellies are inconceivably numerous, and so invisible in the ocean that millions may drift by a boat without ever a one being seen.

These half-inch sea gooseberries glide through the water by means of eight rows of rhythmically beating hairlike combs. Like all the comb jellies, sea gooseberries lack the stinging cells of true jellyfish. They ensnare their prey with pairs of long prehensile tentacles covered with tiny adhesive knobs.

One of the larger of the comb jellies, and one of the few members of the group to show a little color, the six-inch *Beroe* is named for a daughter of the Greek sea god Oceanus. *Beroe* moves through the water like an animated vacuum cleaner, sweeping in anything smaller than itself.

Although the beautiful *Pelagia* jellyfish looks somewhat more substantial than most of its relatives, it nevertheless is more than ninety-five percent water. The jellyfish's mode of swimming can be likened to the opening and closing of an umbrella: rhythmic expansions and contractions of the bell give this nearly weightless creature the slight impetus it needs to keep from sinking.

Jellyfish

Jellyfish also inhabit the upper layers of the ocean in extraordinary numbers, astonishing variety, and many sizes. All of them, from the smallest to the largest, feed vigorously on any crustaceans or fish that touch their stinging tentacles, provided they are not too big. Small jellyfish, often pink, purple, green, or blue, or else clear and colorless, have been seen to swarm for miles in the open ocean. Larger ones are far less numerous but more spectacular.

Watch a jellyfish swimming either in the sea or in a glass container, and you will be fascinated by the regular pulsing of the swimming bell. Small jellyfish pulse rapidly, large ones more slowly, but all do so in much the same manner. The bell-shaped body gently expands, and water fills the cavity of the bell. The outer rim of the body contracts quickly, and the force of the contraction pushes the animal along. In this way the jellyfish propels itself, like a swimmer, through the water. The tentacles trailing from the margin of its bell and from around its mouth form a trap against which other creatures blunder at their peril.

It is important, however, that jellyfish swim more or less upward toward the ocean surface. Even though they may not sink at all when still, they are such active swimmers that they are in danger of swimming downward into the dark deeper water where little food exists and death awaits. So they are equipped with sense organs that guide them away from the darkness below. As a rule there are eight such organs around the outer rim. In some of the smaller jellyfish minute light sensitive organs known as *ocelli*, or "little eyes," cause the creature to swim upward toward the light. Others have tiny gravity-sensitive organs. The effect is the same even though different natural phenomena guide the creatures. However, the ocelli work only in daylight, whereas the gravity organs, the *otocysts*, work all the time.

In any jellyfish, we see a creature perfectly suited to the life it leads. The mass of jelly allows it to stay afloat effortlessly. The pulsating swimming mechanism allows it to move actively through the water in order to feed. Its beautifully symmetrical shape permits it to move easily through the resistant water. The sense organs guide its movements so that it does not mistakenly swim downward for any distance. And the tenacles are arranged so as to encounter food anywhere in the immediate environment.

Colonial swimmers

Two other kinds of delicate but striking forms of oceanic life catch the eye of sailors and naturalists. One group is the siphonophores. The Portuguese man-of-war and the sailor-by-the-wind are siphonophores that are adapted to living at the actual surface of the sea. Their less specialized relatives live below the surface and are rarely seen alive, even though they are common enough in certain oceanic waters. Although acting as a unit, each is made up of individual creatures, some of which are like single jellyfish and others like individual polyps or anemones. Imagine eight or more small jellyfish strung on a thread, acting as swimming bells, with a very small gas-filled float at the upper end of the thread which keeps that end generally upward. Then extend the thread in the other direction and attach a series of small feeding polyps and long stinging tentacles that hang down. The whole net forms a trap into which small animals swim and get caught. The swimming bells draw the creature through the water and increase the likelihood of its bumping into prey. Such creatures or colonies, whichever one calls them, may grow two or three feet long and when in motion look much like "sea serpents." They also resemble organisms known as *salps*, particularly at a stage in the life of the salps when they are called *chain salps*.

This barrel-shaped salp is a much more complex organism than one might think at first glance. Indeed, it is a member of the phylum Chordata, making it one of man's closest relatives among the legions of marine invertebrates.

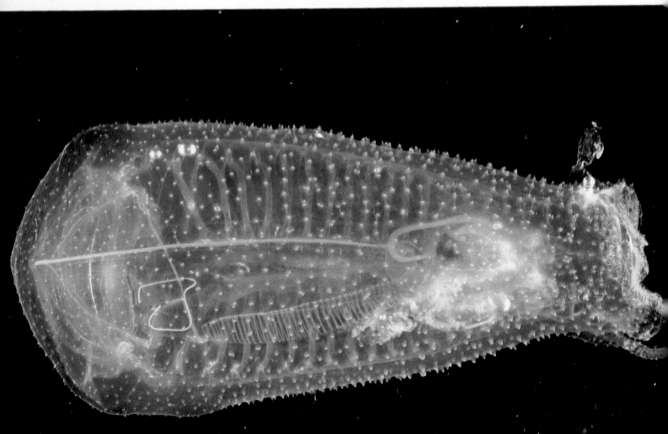

The salp is actually quite unrelated to siphonophores; its close relatives are the sea squirts that live attached to the sea floor. A salp resembles a small barrel open at both ends, with contractile muscle bands around its body that propel it through the water. It sifts food organisms from the water passing through its body. At one stage in its life cycle, however, a salp grows a long chain of new salps from its hinder end by a process of budding. These chains swim along for days until they break up into single individuals.

A relative of the salp, known as *Pyrosoma,* consists of thousands of minute salplike individuals embedded in a tubular mass of jelly open at one end. They cause the colony to glide forward by sucking water into the tube and forcing it out the opened end.

Salps, pyrosomes, and siphonophores, together with jelly-fish and comb jellies of all kinds, are little more substantial than the water they inhabit, in spite of their lovely shapes and delicate colors. In their own way they seem to belong more truly to the sunlit waters of the open ocean than any other creatures, for they are suited to live in no other place.

Pyrosoma is actually a colony of many thousands of small salplike individuals, united into a single organism that may range from thimble size on up to four feet long and ten inches in diameter. Pyrosoma means "fire-body"; and the creature is intensely luminescent, lighting up brightly wherever it is touched. A nineteenth-century naturalist tells of writing his name with his finger on one of the big ones, and seeing his signature appear a few seconds later in letters of fire.

Oceanic swimmers

The abundance of food, whether microscopic plants or semi-microscopic animals, is a boon to any kind of animal able to reach the upper layers of the ocean and stay there. Mollusks, for instance, are typically sea-floor animals. Of a fair size, with body tissues heavier than the water, most of them carry a relatively heavy shell. It is hard for them to get off the bottom. Yet two kinds have done so with such success that they have become important or dominant forms of ocean life. These are the so-called sea butterfly and the squid, both as much mollusks as a snail, but transformed for a very different way of life.

The sea butterflies are better known as *pteropods*, which means "wing-footed," a name that well describes their most outstanding feature. Most still carry a snail-type shell, although it is as light and as thin as possible. Others have lost the shell entirely, for anything that lightens the load lessens the effort necessary to stay afloat. Even so, these rather small creatures sink at once when they stop their vigorous swimming. They swim by means of winglike expansions of the foot that an ordinary snail uses for crawling. The animal flaps the "wings" forward and backward to keep moving upward. Yet in spite of having to fight against gravity as long as they live, enormous numbers of sea butterflies inhabit some parts of the sea. Thousands are often taken in a single haul of a townet. Consequently they are an important source of food for other creatures.

Sea butterflies are among the masters of the seas—the swimmers. These are known as *nekton*, as distinguished from the plankton, which drifts with the current, even though able to swim a bit within it. The members of the nekton are fast and strong enough to move independently of currents. Fish, squid, porpoises, and whales are members of the nekton. Pen-

A close relative of the pteropods or sea butterflies, this heteropod *Carinaria* is another free-swimming snail. It swims upside down, its fragile shell hanging underneath and serving as a keel. The three-inch *Carinaria* is a voracious eater; one individual's stomach was found to contain six fishes, each nearly as long as its captor.

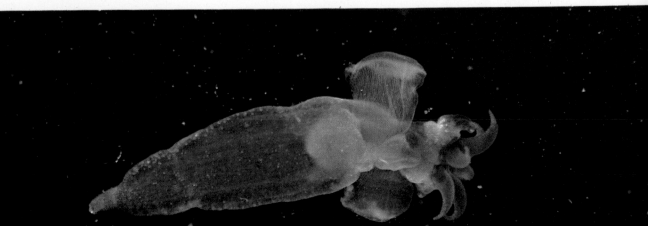

guins, too, should be included. Some have buoyancy, but all have power. And all have color and shading that blend with the sunlit ocean: they are bluish or dark on top so that seen from above they blend with the deep blue darkness of the ocean, and they are light beneath so as to blend with the bright ceiling of the sea when seen from below; and from the side their shading makes them nearly invisible, camouflaged from prey and predator alike. All must drive through the water at considerable speed, displacing it as they go and overcoming the dragging effect of its stickiness. Although inhabitants of the upper layer of the ocean, they live in a very different way from the drifters of the plankton. All have streamlined shapes that reduce the resistance and drag of the water to a minimum, thus allowing them to obtain as much speed as possible. All have powerful body muscles for strong swimming and well-developed sense organs and brains to direct the action of their bodies.

Squid are perhaps the most remarkable of these oceanic swimmers, for like the sea butterflies they are descended from ancient heavy-shelled, slow-moving mollusks of the sea floor. Yet they perform in a most unmolluskan manner. Squid compete with fish on equal terms, and, size for size, they are the faster swimmers. Squid rarely rest on the sea floor. They no longer secrete the heavy lime shells of their ancestors but retain only a horny substance as stiffening for their bodies. They have the streamlined shape of a rocket, for speed is their specialty.

A squid can do everything a fish can do, but in its own way. It is streamlined for speeding backward, not forward like a fish. It has side fins for stability and for planing up or down, like the pectoral fins of a fish or the planes of a submarine. But whereas the fish sculls with a driving thrust of body muscle and tail blade against the resisting water, the squid draws water quickly in through its wide mantle

Squid rank with the fishes as the true masters of the ocean environment. Over short distances, they are the fastest animals in the sea. A remarkably developed nervous system gives them reflexes to match their swimming speed. Squid range in size from specimens an inch or two long to rarely seen deep-sea varieties that may reach an overall length of fifty feet.

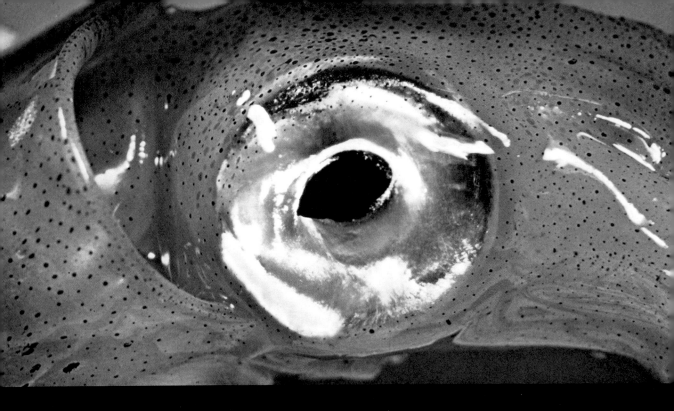

A STARTLING COINCIDENCE

It sometimes happens that two totally unrelated animal groups will travel along parallel evolutionary paths and ultimately arrive at what amounts to the same destination. By far the most striking example of this parallel evolution is the independent development of the camera-type eye by both cephalopods and vertebrates. The cephalopod eye, represented here by the squid (*top left*) and the octopus (*bottom left*), and the vertebrate eye of the sting ray (*top right*) and man (*bottom right*) are more than just similar—they are virtually identical in every detail, even though they are in no

way related to one another. Each of the two
eyes is equipped with a tough, transparent
cornea to admit light. Each has an iris
diaphragm to regulate the amount of light
entering. Each is fluid-filled, to maintain its
spherical shape. Each uses an adjustable lens
to focus a sharp image on a light-sensitive
screen. Each has a complex system of nerve
fibers for transmitting that image to the
brain. Either of these eyes, considered by
itself, is one of the most wonderful of all
objects in the natural world. That evolution
could produce such an object twice is
amazing almost beyond belief.

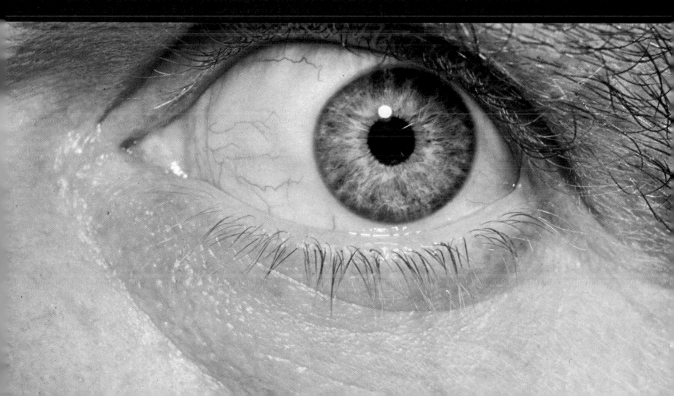

opening and then expels it forcefully through its funnel. This is truly jet propulsion. Water supplies the thrust, while the bands of muscle encircling the body and the water chamber supply the power.

Speed and power of this sort, however, are useful only if under direction, whether the living machinery is that of a squid or that of a fish. Both squid and fish, the one a mollusk and the other a backboned animal, have a well-developed brain, a pair of large camera-type eyes, and complex gravity-sensitive organs of balance, for the control of swimming and for navigation. And, being predators, both are equipped to capture and swallow the creatures they pursue, the squid with its ten sucker-bearing arms and its beak, and the fish with its jaws and teeth. In fact the two kinds of animals are in open competition with one another, even to the extent that some large fish feed on smaller squid, if they can catch them, while squid feed voraciously on fish, especially herring.

The bony fishes

Herring roam the seas, moving in vast schools from place to place as they feed on the planktonic copepods and other small forms of life. Schools of herring or of any other fish of similar size, such as mackerel, present an easy target

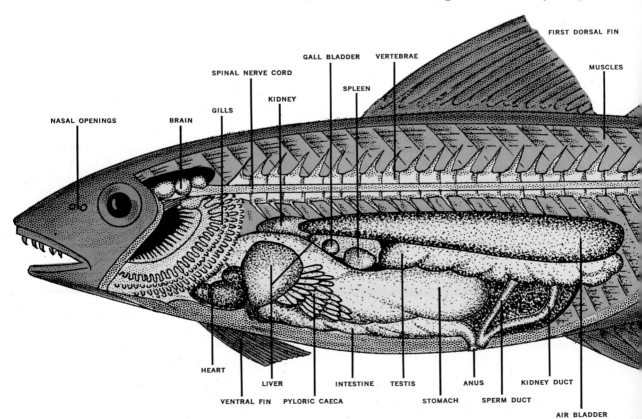

to those that prey on them, and they have many enemies. Some of the fish that prey on them are their own close relatives, although of an outstanding size. They are the fish best known to sports fishermen particularly. Giant members of the herring family, such as tarpon, feed mainly on herring, while the tuna, or tunny, which is a giant mackerel, follows the herring wherever it goes.

No fish seems more streamlined for speed than the tuna. All of its fins are crescent-shaped like the swept-back wings of jet aircraft. They can be either extended for stability or folded back into hollows to eliminate interference with the flow of water over the surface of the torpedo-shaped body. Tuna are among the largest bony fish in the sea and among the fastest. The nonbony fish—the sharks, skates, and rays—grow larger, but they do not compare when it comes to speed.

Most bony fish have air bladders. An air bladder helps a fish to maintain its place in the layer of the ocean to which it is accustomed. By increasing or decreasing the amount of gas in its air bladder, a bony fish can adjust its buoyancy to higher or lower levels in the ocean so that wherever it may be, it does not need to use up energy to maintain its depth. Flying fish have the largest air bladders of all, relative to their body size. These organs not only make them buoyant in the water but also help them to fly.

The typical bony fish is superbly adapted for life in a liquid environment. The air bladder allows it to remain at any level in the water without the effort of swimming. The streamlined shape, rigid skeleton, and powerful musculature all contribute to the animal's ability to move rapidly through the water. The fins provide balance, steering, and braking. The fish "breathes" by drawing water over its gills, charging the blood with oxygen and carrying off waste gases. The bony fish is endowed with all five of the traditional human senses of sight, touch, smell, taste, and hearing, plus a sixth sense provided by the lateral line, which is not fully understood but is apparently associated with the detection of vibrations in the water.

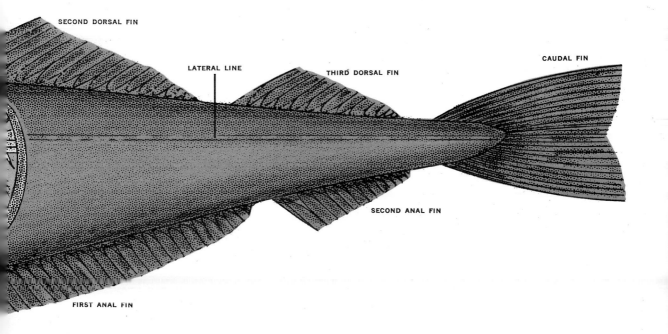

SECOND DORSAL FIN

LATERAL LINE

THIRD DORSAL FIN

CAUDAL FIN

SECOND ANAL FIN

FIRST ANAL FIN

WHAT SHAPE IS A FISH?

When "fish" comes to mind, most of us automatically picture a typical pelagic species like the mackerel (1) or the tuna (2). In a sense, these are the fishiest of the bony fishes—long, sleek, streamlined, built for speed and maneuverability in open waters. But a great many species have departed from this typical body plan, so that the bony fishes exhibit the most diverse range of body shapes and sizes to be found anywhere among the vertebrate animals.

What evolutionary pressure has brought about this divergence? It is tempting to suggest that the bony fishes have developed such a variety of body forms because the ocean environment offers such a variety of habitats. But this argument breaks down when one considers the bony fishes' nearest relatives, the sharks and rays. This ancient, highly successful group lives in exactly the same environment but has settled upon just two basic body plans—the torpedo shape of the sharks, and the pancake shape of the skates and rays.

Whatever underlying evolutionary principle may be at work here, it is safe to say that many of the special adaptations of the bony fishes are concerned with two everyday problems of life in the ocean: to eat and to keep from being eaten.

To this end, the sea horse (3) has departed so far from the typical pelagic shape that it does not even look like a fish. For defense, it relies upon being both inconspicuous and hard to eat; clinging with its prehensile tail, it remains quietly in a thicket of vegetation, its body protected by a layer of horny armor. The filefish (4) mimics the eel-

grass in which it lives, poised head down with its fins undulating in imitation of the eelgrass.

The flatfish (5) are the master mimics of the bony fishes, their remarkable powers of color change rendering them virtually invisible to prey and predator alike. The flying fish (6) eludes its enemies by taking to the air, a medium into which they cannot follow.

The coral reef has given rise to many adaptations. The moray eel (7) is almost more snakelike than fishlike, and its long, sinuous body is ideally suited to foraging in the crags and crannies of the reef. The butterfly fish (8) has evolved a special tubular snout for seeking prey in tiny openings in the coral.

The ocean sunfish (9) has almost given up swimming entirely, preferring to drift with the current near the surface of water, feeding on jellyfish and other slow-moving prey. Its sheer size (eight feet in length and over a ton in weight) plus a three-inch-thick leathery hide protect it from most potential enemies.

Life in deep water presents special problems. Meals may be few and far between, and the gulper (10) is prepared to eat nearly anything that comes along—including animals three times as big as itself. The angler fish (11) attracts prey with a dangling luminescent lure. The luminescence of the lantern fish (12) has not been fully explained, but it may aid in keeping the members of a school together in the dark. At the very bottom of the ocean, the bizarre tripod fish (13) uses its three elongated fin rays as fingers to feel for worms and other burrowers in the mud.

This white-tipped shark displays many of the characteristics that typify the world's 350 species of sharks: the heavy but sinuous body, the gill slits just behind the head, the sturdy triangular fins, the crescent-shaped underslung mouth, the widely spaced nostrils for accurately locating prey by scent. The white-tipped shark reaches fourteen feet and is one of the species considered potentially dangerous to man.

The sharks and rays

Many kinds of sharks and rays live close to the sea floor, but some belong to the open sea as fully as do tuna, tarpon, and the more tropical dolphin fish, bonitos, and other large and colorful bony fish. The nonbony fish stay up by swimming but work harder at it than the bony fish, since they have no air sac. Although suited to one level or another in the ocean, they are generally less adjustable than their bony relatives and must expend energy to maintain their depths.

Blue sharks, man-eaters, tiger sharks, hammerheads, and threshers, all as large as, or larger than, any bony fish, prowl the seas in search of prey, feeding mainly on other fish. On occasion they take small porpoises, sea birds, and turtles. The thresher, especially, feeds in a spectacular manner, using its enormous high-pointing tail with tremendous effect. It is a fast surface swimmer and feeds almost exclusively on herring and mackerel. It swims round and round a school of fish in ever-decreasing circles, lashing with its tail and driving the victims into a compact mass so that they can be gulped down, hundreds at a time.

More extraordinary are the basking sharks of the North Atlantic and the giant manta ray, or devilfish, of tropical seas. Each kind has given up chasing fish, large or small, and

74

has settled, so to speak, for quantities of lesser things. Ranging up to thirty and sometimes forty feet in length, basking sharks cruise through the surface water no faster than a slow walking pace, straining out whatever flows into their enormous gullets. In wintertime, when there is little food to be obtained in this way, they sink to the sea floor and rest until spring. Meanwhile the old strainers in their gills come off, and new sets grow in their place. Their slow cruising speed has inspired the name of basking shark, since from the deck of a passing ship they seem to be motionless.

The fearsome giant manta ray is a very different creature, for it is triangular in shape and more than twenty feet across, weighing over three thousand pounds. Unlike most rays it has completely given up grubbing for a living on the floor of shallow seas and has taken to the surface, more or less flying through the water with its winglike fins. At times it appears to turn complete somersaults in the water, and it will leap several feet into the air, coming down with a bellyflop like a clap of thunder. Mantas have their own method of feeding which is as unusual as the thresher's. The fish has a pair of curious head fins extending forward beyond the eyes and usually carried furled into tight rolls. When the manta meets a swarm of shrimp or small fish, the fins unroll and funnel the food toward the mouth.

A shark's coloration often provides a clue to its preferred habitat. The colors of the four-foot sand shark (*left*) match the bottom of the shallow coastal water it frequents. The twenty-foot blue shark (*right*), on the other hand, is an open-water species; it wears indigo blue above, fading into silvery white below—a color pattern adopted by a great many pelagic animals, from mollusks to whales.

Here is one of the most
beautiful and awesome sights
the sea has to offer: a large
school of mantas flying through
the water with a birdlike
flapping of their enormous
pectoral fins. Manta rays are
also called devilfish, perhaps
because the rolled-up cephalic
fins flanking the mouth suggest
the horns of a devil. These fins
are specialized feeding devices:
when the manta encounters a
school of small fish or crustaceans, the cephalic fins unfurl
and form a funnel that directs
their prey into the mouth.
Mantas tend to pursue their
prey in toward the shore, and
have been known to continue
the chase right up onto the
beach. Despite their size and
frightening appearance, mantas
are harmless to man unless
molested or wounded. Then the
massive pectoral fins can deliver
blows that could crush a
swimmer or capsize a small
boat.

DIVERS IN A CAGE

Much of the marine biologist's work is carried out on dry land in the laboratory, where conditions can be precisely controlled and measurements made with great accuracy. But animals in laboratory tanks and cages never behave quite as they do in their natural environment. To get a true picture of how ocean animals live, there is no substitute for getting into the ocean with them. But when the animals under study are sharks, this approach has an obvious and serious drawback—the subject matter is liable to eat the researcher. Peter Gimbel, a naturalist-photographer anxious to film sharks in their native waters, came up with a clever solution to this problem. Instead of caging the sharks, Gimbel caged himself.

Gimbel's cage, known as the Blue Meridian Diver's Elevator, is shown in action on these two pages. The cage operates without any connection with a mother ship. It is equipped with a self-contained buoyancy system, with controls that can be set to make it ascend or descend at a selected speed or hover at a particular depth. Using the cage, Gimbel and his associates were able to shoot the footage for a documentary film on sharks in the heavily infested waters twenty to one hundred miles off the eastern tip of Long Island. A similar cage is now commercially available and is being put to use in a variety of scientific and industrial applications.

Bottle-nosed dolphins are among the most intelligent of all animals, with a well-developed brain that is somewhat larger than man's. Dolphins take well to captivity. Apparently they even enjoy life in the large open-air tanks of commercial marine aquariums, where their amusing antics make them great favorites with the spectators. In beach areas on both coasts, a human swimmer now and then finds himself being playfully nudged and jostled by a dolphin; probably no harm is intended, but the animal's sheer size (up to twelve feet) makes the experience disquieting for most people.

The whales

The true masters of the seas, however, are the whales. They include not only the great whales, which are now fast disappearing, but also porpoises and dolphins, the smallest and by far the most numerous whales. They have the same shape as fish, and for the same reasons. No other shape permits such speed through water, and the man-sized porpoises and dolphins—there is little difference between them—travel as fast as, or faster than, any other creature in the ocean. Yet in spite of their fishlike shape and their remarkable performance in water, they are warm-blooded air-breathing mammals that bear and nurse their young. Their ancestors long, long ago were four-legged animals that walked on land.

Since that distant time, whales, large and small, have evolved a streamlined body as good as that of any fish, have developed flippers out of forelegs, have lost their hind legs altogether except for rudiments embedded in the tissues, and have exchanged pointed tails for wide horizontal flukes that form driving propellers.

Without any doubt dolphins and porpoises are the most accomplished of all swimming animals. They excel in marine acrobatics, long-distance travel, and navigation; they are highly intelligent and communicate among themselves. You will find a visit to any marine aquarium where these animals are on display a fascinating and exciting experience. In the sea their only enemies, apart from man, are their own kind. The killer whale, which is small for a whale but much larger than a porpoise, is one of the most powerful and ferocious creatures in the ocean, capable of attacking any other animal it sets eyes on.

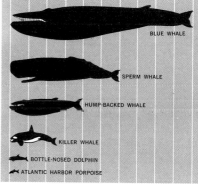

0   10'   20'   30'   40'   50'   60'   70'   80'   90'   100'

Whales range in size from the enormous blue whale, the largest animal ever to live on earth, to porpoises no larger than a man.

81

CABRILLO NATIONAL MONUMENT

Heading north for the summer with her weeks-old calf, this California gray whale releases a puff of moisture-laden air as she surfaces for a breath. California gray whales make an annual 12,000-mile round trip between their breeding grounds off Baja California and their summer quarters in the far North.

Cabrillo National Monument, an 81-acre tract on the tip of Point Loma, is only ten miles from downtown San Diego, yet it offers an unforgettable natural spectacle that cannot be matched anywhere else in the country. At Cabrillo, you can watch whales, the way many people watch birds. Every year, from mid-December to mid-February, thousands of California gray whales, two or three at a time, pass Point Loma on their way to their breeding grounds in the sheltered inlets and lagoons of Baja California. Here, females who had mated the previous year give birth to their fourteen-foot calves, and other females mate with adult males. During March and April, the whales again set forth on the 6000-mile journey to their summer feeding grounds in the Bering Sea. Twice brought to the very brink of extinction by man's greed, the California gray whale is again flourishing under the protection of international law.

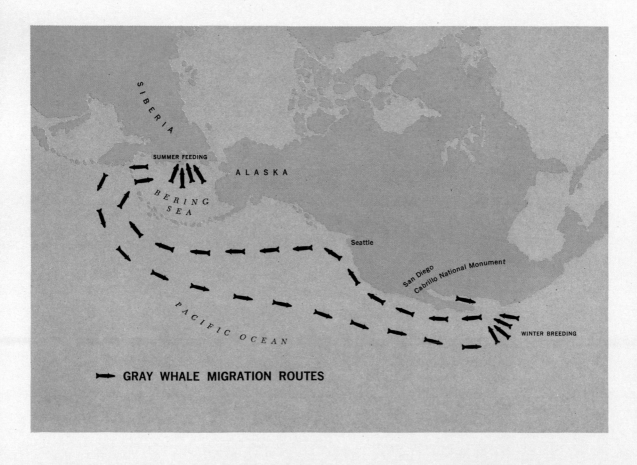

GRAY WHALE MIGRATION ROUTES

With his characteristic high dorsal fin abovewater, Namu the killer whale patrols his cage on the Seattle water front.

KILLER IN A CAGE

On the night of June 22, 1965, a 24-foot, 5-ton killer whale became trapped in a salmon net in the waters off Namu, British Columbia. Six days later the whale was purchased from the net's owners by Edward I. Griffin, the operator of a commercial aquarium in Seattle, Washington. On July 28, after a 450-mile journey in a floating pen, the whale (by then named Namu, after the site of his capture) was established on public view alongside Pier 56 on Seattle's water front.

Namu was an instant box-office success. Before the end of September, more than 100,000 customers had come to watch the captive killer in his 40- by 60-foot floating cage. Namu apparently took well both to captivity and to show business —under the tutelage of Griffin and his staff, the ponderous whale was soon earning his 400-pound daily ration of salmon by performing a repertory of tricks that delighted his crowds of daily visitors.

Although the captive killer whale was primarily a money-making venture, Griffin was generous in making Namu available to interested researchers. As a result, much new information has been added to our knowledge of ocean mammals.

Namu's owner climbs aboard for a ride. The whale loved having his tough hide scrubbed with a long-handled brush.

The killer whale is generally considered the most fearsome predator in the ocean. It has a very high order of intelligence and when attacking its victims often displays great cunning and ingenuity. Its appetite is gargantuan—the opened stomach of one dead killer revealed 32 full-grown seals. The animal is said to share with man a characteristic nearly unknown in the rest of the natural world: it kills for pleasure as well as for food.

How dangerous are killer whales to humans? The evidence is conflicting and inconclusive, but most observers feel that, given the opportunity, the killer would not hesitate to add man to his menu.

Griffin disagrees, and his personal experience with Namu backs him up to some extent. After a period of cautious preliminaries, Griffin spent countless hours in the water with Namu, and he feels that something approaching rapport and mutual affection developed between himself and the whale. But before conclusions can be drawn about killer whales in general, two points should be considered: Griffin is a skilled and experienced animal handler; and Namu's disposition may or may not be typical of his species.

The story of Namu ended in abrupt tragedy on the night of July 9, 1966. Perhaps in response to his seasonal breeding urge, the captive killer tried to escape. He succeeded in ramming a 25-foot hole in the side of his pen but became hopelessly entangled in the twisted and broken cables. He was discovered the next morning, the victim of a danger that is ever-present for the mammals that have returned to the sea: Namu had drowned.

Killer whales, like porpoises and dolphins (to which they are related), are among nature's most intelligent animals. In captivity, Namu quickly learned to perform stunts like this.

Namu rolls over on his back and daintily accepts his favorite delicacy, an entire full-grown salmon.

The migrating plankton

When you go out from shore in a ship, the ocean does not become very deep until you pass over the edge of the continental shelf. The edge may be more than a hundred miles off the Atlantic coast of the American continent but is close inshore off the Pacific coast. The sea may look deep from the deck of a ship, but if the 1250-foot-high Empire State Building were placed on the sea floor anywhere on the shelf, more than half of it would stand out of water. The water over the shelf is well inhabited all the way to the bottom.

A few miles beyond the continental shelf, though, the sea may be a mile deep. In the deepest places there is more than six miles of water above the sea floor, deep enough to sink Mount Everest out of sight. (Mount Everest is over five miles high.) Most of the ocean is deep, far deeper than the depth to which light can penetrate even in the clearest water.

In the upper, lighted zone of the sea most of the inhabitants move up and down regularly with the alternation of night and day. Herring fishermen shoot their drift nets at

Why do virtually all members of the animal plankton undertake extensive daily vertical migrations, rising toward the surface at night, sinking into deeper waters during the day? Each species—and the three shown here are only typical examples—shows a characteristic pattern for these daily trips. There can be no doubt that this unusual behavior is of profound importance in the lives of these animals, but scientists have not yet been able to offer a full explanation of its significance, despite an enormous amount of research on the problem.

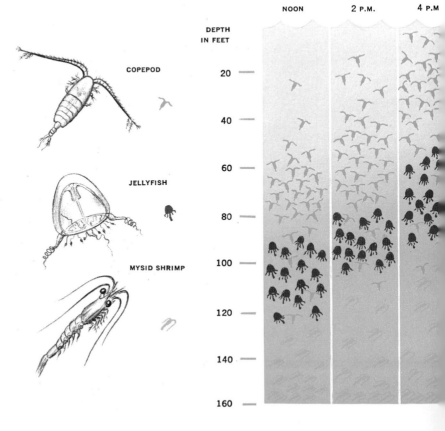

night, because only at night does the "herring feed" plankton rise close enough to the surface in numbers sufficient to attract the herring.

This vertical migration of the plankton has long been one of the mysteries of the sea. Throughout the year the animal plankton rises by night and sinks by day, in tune with the turning of the earth and the setting and rising of the sun. Ever since they first began to use townets, naturalists have usually made much larger catches of plankton near the surface at night than during the day, whereas townets at deeper levels caught much more during the day than at night.

Today we know that most of the small, free-swimming animals of the plankton make extensive up-and-down migrations. This fact is puzzling because diatoms and other phytoplankton, which flourish only in the uppermost layer, cannot migrate. The sea pasture remains in place, but the animals do not. As dusk sets in, the small animals that have been spending the daytime hours at some depth all begin to swim upward. By the time the last light has faded from the sky, the surface layers of the water, so empty before, are a teem-

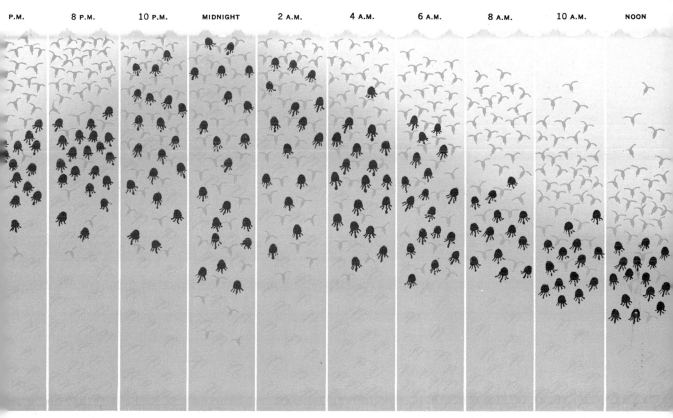

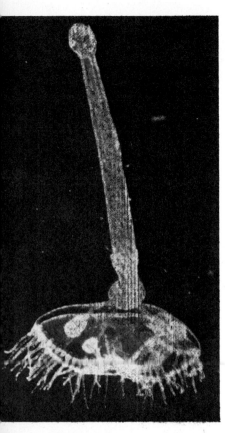

A small predacious jellyfish, *Obelia*, has captured and is devouring an inch-long arrowworm. Both of these animals take part in the daily vertical migration that remains one of the unsolved puzzles of the plankton community.

ing soup of planktonic animal life. Those creatures that were not so deep to start with arrive sooner than the others, but by midnight and until dawn the upper layer of the sea is rich. The sinking begins with the first predawn light of the new day, however, and all the animals descend to deeper water as the sun gets high.

Why does the plankton migrate?

It is remarkable that so small a creature as a copepod, such as *Calanus*, a small fraction of an inch long, can swim up and down as much as several hundred feet each day. All the tiny planktonic creatures, including copepods, opossum shrimps, arrowworms, small jellyfish, and many others, expend a great deal of energy in this migration. The changing brightness of light entering the sea appears to regulate the migrations, with strong light signaling the downward swim. But why does the animal plankton migrate in this manner? Since the source of food remains where it was, what good does it do these creatures to shift up and down?

One explanation is that they swim up to feed in the sea pasture only at night because the darkness will hide them from their enemies. This probably is not so, because many of these animals are luminescent and seem actually to advertise their presence. Another explanation, which may well be the correct one, is that vertical migration is navigation of a sort, not so much to go somewhere as to avoid being carried too far away by ocean currents, or at least to avoid being carried away too rapidly. If all the drifting life of the surface waters took only a one-way journey in the current to distant and probably unsuitable places, it is hard to see how the various kinds of animals could survive. It now seems likely that they rise and fall like the early balloonists who took advantage of air currents going in different directions by going up or down to find the air current they wanted.

The surface layers of the ocean are nearly always traveling faster than the lower layers, and they often travel in different directions. An animal that can swim to left or right for only a few hundred feet will be carried along as though it had not moved at all. Yet if it sinks down one or two hundred feet into a current going another way, and then up again the same day, it may well counteract the drift, and in any case slow down the rate of drift.

90

Some of the most abundant planktonic crustaceans in the Antarctic Ocean, the shrimplike euphausids, undoubtedly use the currents to maintain their position. In the Antarctic, cold surface water flows northward away from the melting ice as a current extending to a depth of about three hundred feet. Below it there is a warmer current flowing in the opposite direction, southward toward the pole, to take its place. Certain kinds of these crustaceans stay in one location, in effect, by making a vertical migration of about six hundred feet every day, spending the night in the surface current traveling north, and by day traveling south in the reverse current down below.

Life in the depths

As we go down into the ocean, below the surface layer of sunlit water, we enter a region that is virtually the same throughout the globe. Light is faint, scattered, or absent altogether, and the water is cold all the way to the bottom and from the poles to the equator. The distance from the top layer to the ocean bottom is more than a mile. This enormous body of water is continuous from ocean to ocean, representing an individual zone of life that is monotonously cold, calm, dark, and short of food. Yet living creatures inhabit it down to the greatest depths, where pressure is tremendous. Growth, survival, and reproduction are far more difficult in these circumstances than they are near the surface, where there is light to see by and where food of one sort or another is generally abundant. In the dark it is hard to see either friend or foe; and because food is scarce, there are far fewer things to see. Obtaining food of any kind or finding a mate becomes a great problem.

All food must originate in the uppermost layer of the ocean, where it is manufactured by green cells in the presence of sunlight. What reaches the dark depths are the crumbs from the table, so to speak: the lost, the dying, and the dead remains of the various members of the plankton, both plant and animal, that sink into the immensity below. All the inhabitants live in a calm, still world disturbed only by the movements of the animals themselves, and all are adjusted to the darkness, the difficulty in obtaining food, and the low temperature, which remains just above freezing. The circumstances change, however, as depth increases.

Even in the clearest water, sunlight can penetrate only so far. Furthermore, each of the spectral colors that together form the white light of the sun is absorbed at a different rate, with red disappearing first and blue persisting to the greatest depth. The diagram below illustrates this, and is based on measurements taken by William Beebe from his bathysphere off the Bermuda coast. He observed that red light faded into nothingness in the first 59 feet. Yellow was gone within 328 feet, and green did not reach beyond 787 feet. All that remained was a faint blue-black light down to 1706 feet, below which the water was pitch black—to human eyes, at least.

FEET
----59
--------328
----------787
--------------1706

That protective coloration—the ability to blend into the surrounding environment—can be a vital element in the survival of a species is dramatically illustrated by the prawns shown on these two pages. The species on this page inhabits the well-lit upper waters of the ocean. Because of its bluish coloration and its translucency, a potential predator might easily overlook it.

To begin with, the light disappears not all at once but gradually and color by color. Since most sea animals either are searching for food or are in danger of being eaten, or both, there is advantage in not being seen. Where there is plenty of daylight, many of the planktonic creatures are transparent. Others that are too thick or too dense to see through, such as fish and squid, are merged into their surroundings by camouflaging color in their skin. Squid can change their color rapidly and drastically according to the need of the moment and in fact do so to some extent continually; they scintillate as they swim along, so that now you see them, now you don't. Yet just a short distance below the surface the light not only is much weaker but has a different quality. In less than seventy feet the water has absorbed all the red light so that to a fish or a skin diver everything appears to be a bluish green. At this depth, and below, it is safe for an animal to be red, for without any red light left to be reflected, a red body looks much the same as black. Yellow is the next to go, then green, and at depths below a thousand feet all that is left is some weak blue light. This is the twilight zone, where there may be just enough light to see by, if eyes are good, but much less than is needed for the growth of plants. Here, and at greater depths, fish are black and prawns (shrimp) are red, which amounts to the same thing, just as persons wearing black coats and red coats would look dark if you saw them out in a night lit only by the stars.

Eyes in the deep

The creatures of the twilight zone are remarkable in other ways. Whether red or black, or with silver scales as in many of the fish, they make use of all the light there is. Their eyes are usually exceptionally large. In deeper water no natural light at all can penetrate, and some fish and some prawns are blind, with degenerated eyes like those of cave animals. Both fish and squid have camera-type eyes, however. This kind of eye works differently from the so-called compound eye of crustaceans and, unlike the compound eye, has responded to the need to see in the dark. The saucerlike eyes of deepwater fish and squid are usually large

The prawn shown on this page lives in the depths, where only the faintest suggestion of violet-blue light ever penetrates. Under such lighting conditions, this creature's bright red shell appears jet black, making it as invisible as the velvety black fishes that also dwell in this realm.

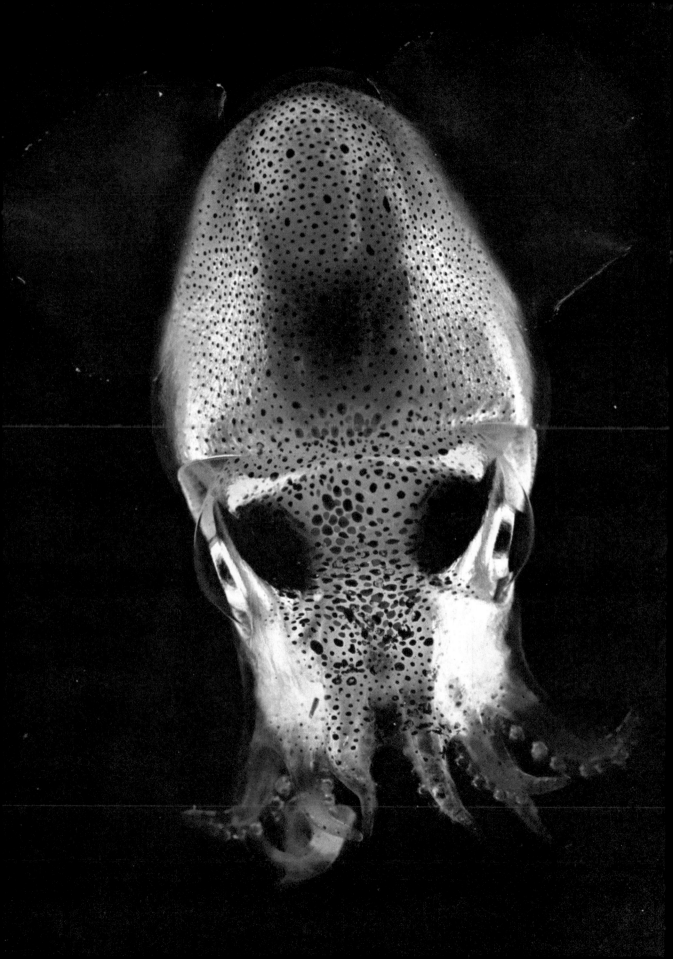

The enormous owllike eyes of this squid mark it as a dweller of deep water, where the sense of sight, to be useful at all, must gather and concentrate an immense amount of light. Some species of these deep-sea squid have evolved an interesting defense mechanism: when a predator threatens, the squid ejects a cloud of brightly luminous "ink" and darts away, leaving the enemy dazzled and confused.

in relation to the size of their bodies and may occupy almost the entire sides of their heads. Eyes of this sort may detect the faintest glimmer of light.

Some deep-sea fish and squid have progressed even further in the development of their camera eyes. Besides being exceptionally large, the eyes are turned upward, so that they constantly watch the water overhead as the animals swim slowly along in the customary horizontal position. More than this, the eyes are greatly elongated and are in fact telescopic. These creatures literally scan the water above with living binoculars, watching for the dark silhouettes of smaller animals against the slightly luminous blue-black background overhead.

Living flashlights

Even though little or no light from the surface reaches the depth at which these animals live, this deep-sea zone has light of its own, produced by the animals themselves. The living light given off by surface drifters such as dinoflagellates, comb jellies and jellyfish is a simple diffuse flashing that occurs when the creatures are physically disturbed. The deep-sea animals not only produce cold light of a similar sort but do so by means of special organs located in particular places on the head or sides of the body. These organs, present in deep-sea fish, squid, and prawns alike, are similar to flashlights, constructed somewhat like an eye in reverse. Each kind of animal has evolved this type of living flashlight or lantern independently of the others, just as camera eyes have evolved independently in mollusks and in animals with backbones. The light organ has a lens in front of the light source and a concave reflector behind, with a backing of black pigment. The light comes from a mass of cells that liberate cold light as a result of chemical activity. Some

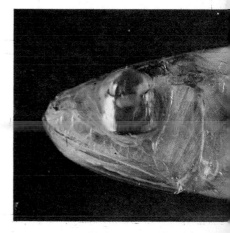

With eyes like upturned binoculars, this deep-sea fish constantly scans the faintly lit waters overhead for a potential meal.

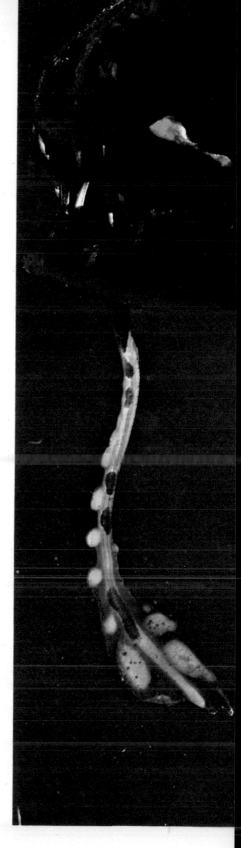

Bioluminescence plays a variety of roles in the deepwater world. Like a fisherman's lure, the luminous chin ornament on this fish (*right*) attracts prey. The distinctive photophore pattern on the squid (*left*) may serve to bring members of the same species together for mating.

prawns and the shrimplike euphausids usually have ten light organs: one pair behind the eyes, two pairs on the side of the body, and four on the underside of the tail. Even more spectacular are some deep-sea cuttlefish, close relatives of the squid, which have over twenty light organs in various parts of the body. Most of these organs throw a white light, but two located near the eyes are deep blue, while another pair, on the underside of the body, are red. Fish are just as well equipped, and many have a long row of light organs along the whole length of the body on each side, not unlike the portholes of a ship.

All these creatures are small animals, a few inches long at the most. They are primarily inhabitants of the twilight zone, or middle ocean, rather than the truly great depths. Fish that live deeper are just as small, but they are black all over, without the silver sides of the middle-ocean kinds. Many do not have living lanterns, and their eyes are very small or actually blind. Many of these fish, however, have relatively enormous mouths, in some cases capable of swallowing another fish of equal size. They would be strange and forbidding monsters of the deep if they were large. Being small, they are merely bizarre curiosities, although of very great interest to a biologist.

Light organs, or *photophores*, are so well developed and are possessed by so many kinds of deep-sea creatures that they must serve a useful purpose. What this purpose may be is still a mystery. Possibly they serve as recognition signs so that the creatures can come together at times for mating. This has not been proved, but getting together is certainly a problem for animals that live in the dark.

One kind of angler fish, a small deep-sea fish belonging to the same peculiar group as the fishing-frog fish of the sargassum weed, lacks such light organs and employs what appears to be a desperate remedy to overcome the difficulty. Since such angler fish develop and grow up in the dark and the chance of a male and female ever encountering one an-

Needle-studded jaws and multicolored photophores are the hallmarks of the deep-sea viperfish.

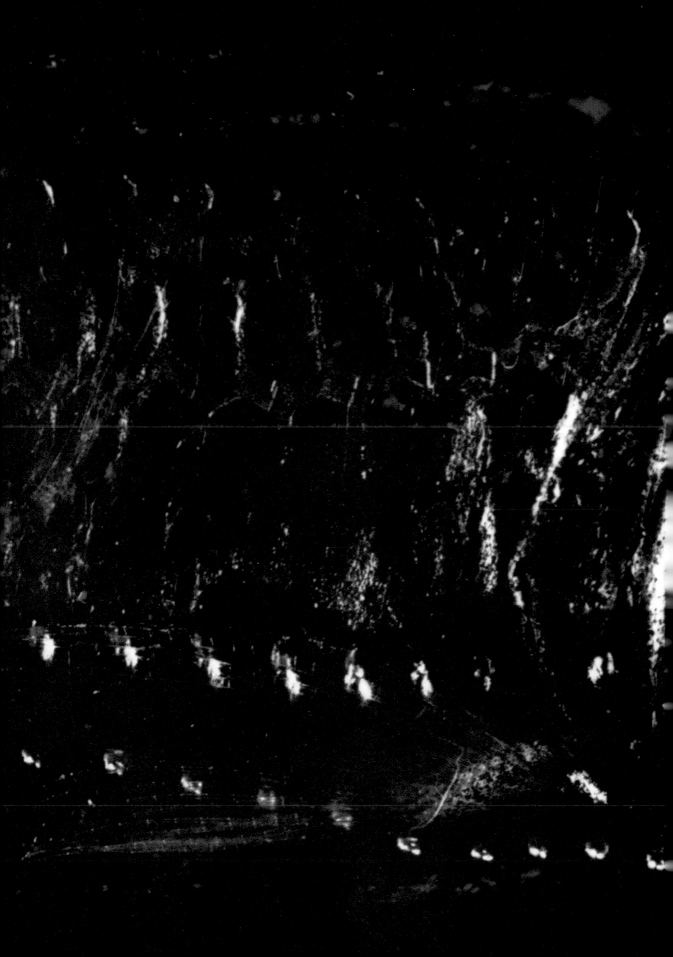

other is so slim, when the two sexes do happen to meet, they join together at once even though they may be far from mature. Whenever a juvenile male meets a female, it bites into her skin wherever it can, on the sides of the body or on the head, and never lets go. It becomes a dwarf male parasite from then on, nourished by the blood of the female; but as a penalty its own head degenerates, leaving the attached body as little more than a piece of living machinery for fertilizing eggs when the time comes. The free life of the male is sacrificed to serve the future of the species.

So far as we can tell, the lantern-bearing fish and mollusks of the middle ocean invade the upper layers during the night, presumably to feed on the rich plankton there. It is possible that the lantern display attracts the food organisms toward the feeder or perhaps illuminates the surrounding water sufficiently for the fish to see them, but these again are only guesses. One fish has a deep pocket on each side of its head, containing a mass of luminescent bacteria that glow continually and cannot be shut off. However, over each pocket there is a fold of black skin that is thrown back and forth like a shutter, so that the whole structure becomes an on-and-off searchlight as the fish darts at its prey.

The mysterious false bottom

Until fairly recently marine naturalists have believed that with increasing depth from the surface the plankton becomes scarcer and scarcer. Certainly in the great depths there is very little, and animal life as a whole is scarce. Yet in the

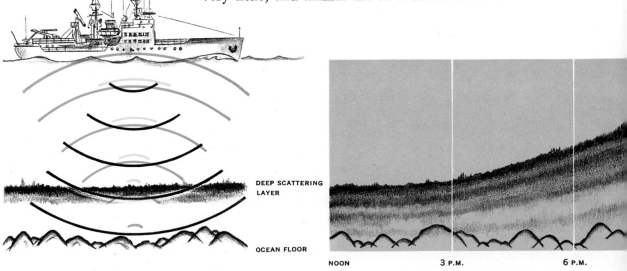

DEEP SCATTERING LAYER

OCEAN FLOOR

NOON   3 P.M.   6 P.M.

intermediate depths something is present that is by no means fully understood. During World War II echo-sounding equipment was used in surface ships for detecting submarines and has since been employed for mapping the ocean floor in all parts of the world. Through echo sounding, oceanographers have discovered great ridges and flat-topped mountains rising high above the sea floor but still far below the surface. Echo sounders beam sound waves downward from a ship and measure the time it takes for the waves to reflect off whatever solid surfaces there are below and to return to the ship. These readings are registered on a slowly unrolling band of paper and give observers on the ship a continuous indication of the depths of the reflecting material below them. Echo sounders are now widely used by commercial fishermen for detecting schools of fish.

The puzzling discovery is that a sound-reflecting layer exists all over the ocean at a depth of about twelve hundred to fifteen hundred feet, which is roughly the location of the so-called twilight zone. This reflecting layer is now known as the "deep scattering layer," a name that merely describes its record on the echo-sounder recorder and gives no indication of what causes it. The layer gives the impression of a false sea bottom, false because it is certain that one or more miles of dark ocean lie beneath. Whatever is responsible for the sound reflection must be enormously abundant, spread densely and in very wide patches, for the reflecting layer stretches unbroken for hundreds of miles.

Furthermore the reflecting layer rises at night and sinks by day, and so there seems to be no doubt that some sort of animal life must be the cause. However, the choice is lim-

The puzzling deep scattering layer that creates the illusion of a false bottom on echo-sounding gear rises during the night and sinks during the day. This strongly suggests that it is of animal origin, and that some sort of vertical migration is involved, similar to that displayed by the zooplankton at much shallower depths. But the identity of the animals responsible is yet to be established.

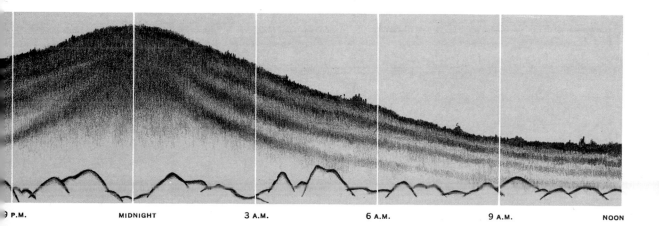

3 P.M.　　　MIDNIGHT　　　3 A.M.　　　6 A.M.　　　9 A.M.　　　NOON

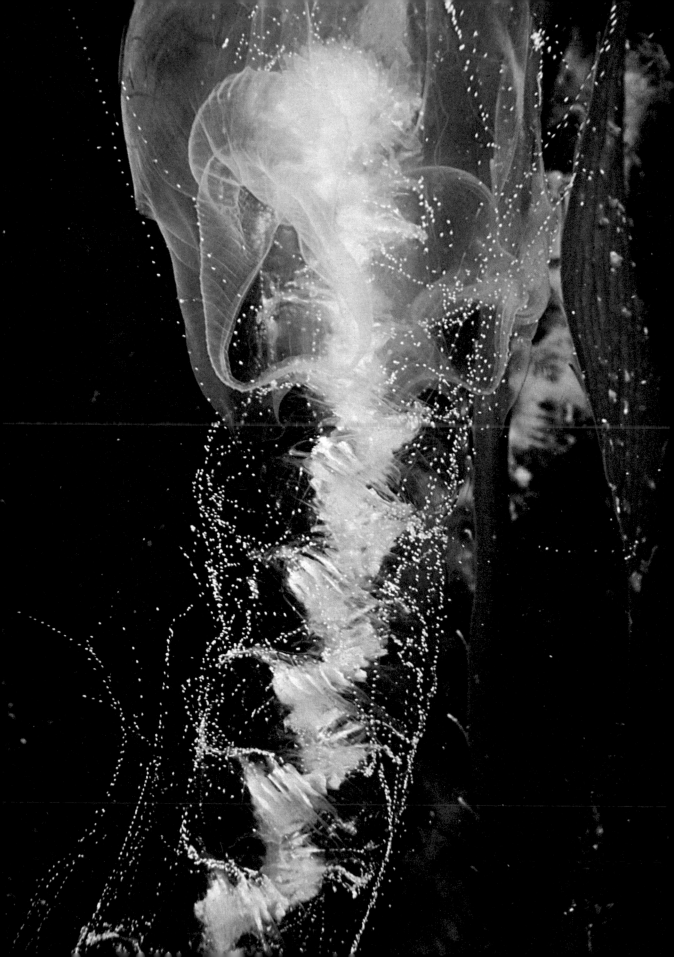

ited, since not all kinds of sea life will reflect sound. The most probable reflectors are the hard outer surface of crustaceans, the swim bladders of fish, and the gas chambers of siphonophores and cuttlefish. For such creatures to act as a sounding board, millions of them would have to be present in relatively small areas, although any that were present would send back an echo of a sort. Television cameras lowered to the proper depth show almost nothing, but possibly the apparatus scares the creatures away before they can be seen. Plankton nets towed vertically up through the deep scattering layer show nothing unusual. It is unlikely that small deep-sea fish of the kind just discussed are numerous enough, for otherwise they should be captured much more often.

One likely explanation comes from observers who have gone down to great depths and back in the bathyscaphe *Trieste* off the coast of Southern California. They report that when passing through the deep scattering layer they saw innumerable almost transparent siphonophores. Each had its minute float, or gas chamber, and line of swimming bells, pointing upward, and its long cord bearing the stinging tentacles drifting out more or less horizontally through the water as far as the eye could see. Creatures such as these move vigorously when disturbed and are not readily caught in deep-sea nets. If they do constitute the main source of the deep scattering layer, then throughout almost all of the ocean, at about the lower limit to which any light from the surface can penetrate, there is a continuous trap for any small creatures that may move upward or downward in this zone. Only the seas of the Arctic and Antarctic appear to be without it. Every night it rises toward the surface, and each day it sinks down to its customary level about twelve hundred feet below. Such a vertical migration suggests that the living community of the middle ocean, as a whole, rises and sinks like the plankton of the upper level and that the predatory siphonophores keep pace with it.

Do countless millions of siphonophores like this one constitute portions of the deep scattering layer, the mysterious false bottom that confounds oceanographers' electronic instruments? Only further exploration of the ocean's depths will provide the answer.

The Bountiful Ocean

The life of the ocean is forever changing. It varies from place to place, and it changes with the time of year. Some regions of the ocean are abundantly rich in life, and others are not. The Norwegians who sailed the *Kon-Tiki* raft halfway across the Pacific from the coast of South America, taking a course just south of the equator, found abundant ocean life around them all the way. But Sir Francis Drake, sailing the *Golden Hind* all the way from the California coast to the East Indies, did not see a single fish during sixty-eight days. There are deserts in the ocean as well as on land, in the sense that large areas are virtually empty of life. And as on land the seasons play their part, for both plant and animal life is much more in evidence during spring and summer than it is in winter.

As the earth turns, the seasons follow one another with absolute regularity. Yet the seasons are not the same the world over, and the typical spring, summer, autumn, and winter so familiar to most people are strongly marked only in the temperate, or middle, latitudes of the Northern and Southern Hemispheres. In the tropics and semitropics the sea-

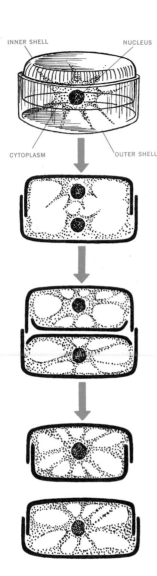

INNER SHELL   NUCLEUS

CYTOPLASM   OUTER SHELL

Diatoms normally reproduce by a simple division process. First, the nucleus divides and the cytoplasm separates into two masses, each containing a nucleus. Then two new inner shells are secreted. Finally, the two new cells break away from each other and become independent organisms.

sonal change is hardly noticeable. Within the Arctic Circle to the north and the Antarctic Circle to the south, the yearly change is mainly from one long winter night, lit only by the moon and stars, to one long summer day during which the sun never sets. Moreover, the seasons in the Northern and Southern Hemispheres are in alternation with each other: when it is summer in the north, it is winter in the south. All this affects life in the sea as much as it affects life on land. The march of the seasons, except in the warm and equable tropics, brings with it a regular succession of plant and animal life in the ocean.

The arrival of spring

Whether on land or sea, spring is the season when the sun is climbing high in the heavens, the air is warming up after the cold of winter, and the days are already long. Every day the light gets stronger and lasts a little longer, and all green life that depends upon it bursts into luxuriant growth. Throughout the oceans each microscopic single-celled plant of the plankton, whether brown, yellow, or green, whether diatom or dinoflagellate, divides into two cells at least once during the course of a day. Day after day the plants more than double their number, and by the end of a month at this rate each original single cell has multiplied to over two hundred billion. If you pull a fine net through the sea in spring, its meshes will soon become clogged with microscopic plants because the diatoms and flagellates are so dense. This is the so-called spring blooming of the seas, to be seen also in lakes and ponds, and at no other time of year will the sea pasture be so rich. And wherever it occurs, the animal plankton benefits accordingly.

During early spring, temporary members of the animal plankton are by far the most noticeable, particularly in coastal waters and shallow seas where sea-floor creatures are abundant. The microscopic and semimicroscopic forms of animal life that you can find in a net are mainly planktonic larval stages of worms, clams, sea snails, starfish, and crustaceans. Along rocky coasts the seas swarm with the free-swimming larvae of the acorn barnacles that encrust the rocks with their white protective fortresses of lime. Farther from the shore and stretching far across the ocean, the upper waters become full of the young of the plankton

106

copepod *Calanus,* together with the young of many smaller creatures. And everywhere, inshore and far out at sea, young fish hatch in profusion, to feed on the rich pasturage of diatoms and the like, or on the teeming young and adult copepods. The massive growth of the vegetation permits the animal plankton's burst of life.

By late spring or early summer the great crop of drifting microscopic plants diminishes. Much of it has been eaten by the small planktonic animals, and much has sunk to deeper levels where other creatures can consume it. The animal life of the upper layers, however, has had its annual boost, and throughout the summer the various members of the zooplankton grow up and feed on one another. Many types of larvae continue to join the plankton from the sea-floor community down below, while those that came earlier and have managed to escape the hazards of being eaten or drifting away as they mature leave the plankton and sink down to take up their adult way of life.

During the spring bloom, plant plankton, or phytoplankton, multiplies at an incredible rate, forming a lush sea pasture for the small and larval animals that will soon arrive in great numbers. The phytoplankton sample shown here (magnified seventy-five times) consists mainly of several species of diatoms.

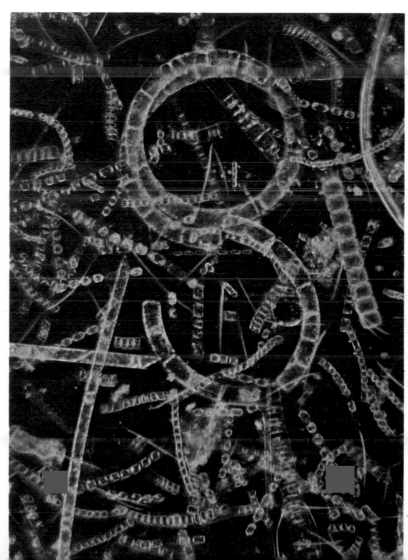

Here is the living plankton world, magnified seventy times, as it appears during the late spring in the cold waters of the Atlantic Ocean. Diatoms are everywhere, in bewildering variety, and at least half a dozen different species are visible in this picture alone. Feeding on these miniature green plants is an equally wide variety of animal plankton, and more will follow soon as floating eggs continue to hatch out larvae. As they grow, these tiny creatures must cast their skins, just as crabs and lobsters do, and some of these outgrown skins can be seen here. Some of these animals, such as the copepods, will be permanent members of the plankton community. Others, such as the acorn barnacle and the bristle worm, are only temporary residents and will eventually take up life on the ocean bottom.

1. Adult copepod
2. Bristle-worm egg
3. Copepod larva
4. Acorn barnacle larva
5. Unidentified egg
6. Cast skin of larva
7. Diatom

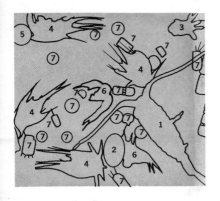

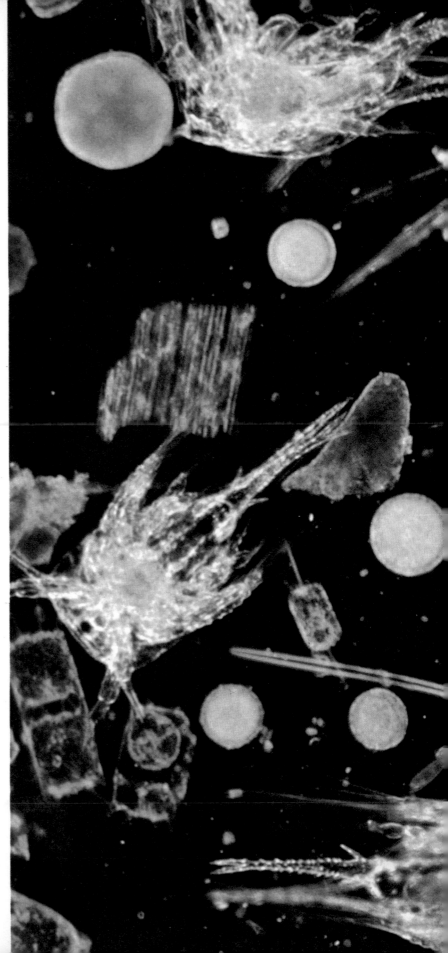

In winter, plankton is sparse and consists mostly of animal forms (shown in white). In spring, plant forms (shown in blue) predominate. Plant growth declines in summer, but animal plankton reaches a peak. Finally, after a brief fall plant bloom, plant and animal populations decline to their low winter levels.

And so the succession goes on. Each month of the spring and summer sees a plankton community that differs from that of the preceding month in both the kinds and the quantities of its members. Finally, in autumn, when one would expect the plankton to be dying down with the approach of winter, there is another outburst of plant life, though not so great as in the spring. After that the plankton as a whole almost disappears, with little plant life and only a small number of planktonic animals surviving through the cold, dull winter months to form the stock for the next spring's blooming.

When summer comes

It is clear that the number of animals able to exist in the sea depends on the quantity of plant life. Great changes or differences in the animal life from place to place or from time to time can be traced to increase or decrease in the plankton vegetation. The hosts of small creatures that reach maturity during the summer consume a large amount of the vegetation that first blooms in the spring. But this grazing accounts only partly for the diminishing of the plant growth during summer. We have to examine the seawater itself to find the explanation for the changing numbers of plants.

To grow, all plants require light, water, and mineral salts. Land plants obtain their minerals from the soil, marine plants from the surrounding seawater. Since seawater is full of dissolved minerals, it would seem logical to expect that it contains an abundance of all the necessary salts. Yet this is not the case. Certain chemicals are in short supply, both in soil and in the sea. These are the nitrates and phosphates, the so-called fertilizer minerals necessary to promote the growth and productivity of so many agricultural crops.

No matter how abundant all other necessities for growth may be, as soon as any single necessity runs short, growth declines and stops. On land it may be a lack of heat and light that causes the plants to stop growing, as in areas where winters are cold, or it may be a lack of water, as in deserts; or, when light and water are adequate, it may be a lack of one kind of mineral or another. The same holds true for plants of the ocean. There is always plenty of water, to be sure, but light may or may not be sufficient. And in spite of the great concentration of the many minerals that

110

make seawater so salty, nitrates and phosphates are relatively scarce.

In winter, except in the tropics, the sun is low and most of its rays are reflected from the surface of the ocean instead of penetrating into the water. Consequently, the plants cannot grow, even though all the necessary salts may be present. As the sun gets higher with the coming of spring, the energy of the sunlight becomes available to the plants, and they start to grow and multiply. Yet within a month or so the plants use up nearly all the fertilizer salts, the phosphates and nitrates; and in spite of the intense light, plants stop increasing. From then on the sea creatures are on their own, so to speak, building from one kind of animal life to another but all based on the quantity of plant life consumed during the short period it was available.

The late blooming

The brief spurt of plant growth in autumn, however, is a sign that the stage is being set for the great renewal of the growth of plant and animal life in the following spring, for it results from one of the most important changes that the ocean undergoes during the course of every year.

During the summer, when the sun rises high overhead, the surface layer of the ocean warms up. Heat does not pass easily from one layer of water to another. The layer of water warmed directly by rays of the sun gets warmer and warmer, while the layer beneath remains cold. But even though the waters of the two layers do not mix, there is a transfer of vital nutrients from one to the other.

Throughout the spring and summer all the dead and dying animals and plants of the upper layer, together with other organic remains, continually sink down into the lower layer, building up the supply of the important salts there. Thus there is light enough for plant growth in the upper layer, but no longer sufficient salts; there are plenty of nutrient salts in the lower layer, but not enough light for plants to use them.

In the autumn, when the sunlight is weaker, the upper layer of the ocean cools and can mix with the lower layer, and the autumnal gales mix the water masses together. Fresh supplies of nutrient salts reach the top, and plant growth resumes, but too late in the year to do much good: as winter

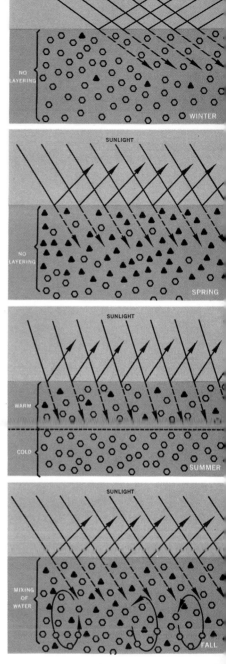

Ocean plants depend on light and minerals, which vary with season. In winter, minerals (hexagons) are plentiful; but light is dim, and so plant life (triangles) is sparse. In spring, minerals and light are plentiful, and plants flourish. By summer light is strong but minerals are depleted, and plant growth declines. Autumn storms bring up new minerals from the depths, allowing a burst of plant growth.

111

comes and the light continues to weaken, plant growth ceases for lack of light. The sea, now well fertilized all the way to the surface, must wait till the following year before its world of microscopic plants can take advantage of the again favorable conditions.

Deserts in the sea

Such is the seasonal cycle of the plankton in cool temperate oceans. Early investigators thought that in the tropics the year-round warmth of the surface waters would encourage a vigorous growth of plankton organisms throughout the year, as in tropical forests. So it was surprising when the townets of marine biologists showed a very small catch at all times, except in unusual circumstances. There is certainly sufficient light to support plant growth in these waters at all periods of the year. The explanation for the poor showing seems to be that the sea is warmed to a greater depth without any sharp separation from a cold layer underneath, no reservoir of fertilizer salts accumulates below, and there are no spring or autumn gales to mix the waters. Ocean plant life, and therefore the animal plankton dependent on it, grows in the tropics only to the limits of the fertilizer salts already present without any regular replenishment. This amounts to a thin crop at all times, instead of a rich one every spring and practically nothing during winter.

Wherever you see the beautiful deep blue color of the tropical ocean, you know that comparatively little life is present, unless it is where currents come together and the

Most of us assume automatically that warm tropical seas teem with life, but we are very much mistaken. Despite the thick plant growth along this Hawaiian shore, the clear blue water is a barren desert, almost empty of life.

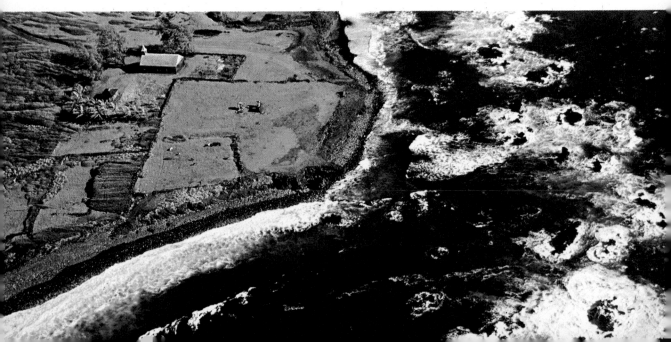

life from a wide area has been gathered into a narrow strip. The deep blue is like the blue of the sky and results from the scattering of light by water molecules. The emptier the water, the bluer it seems and the farther down the light can penetrate because there is less to stop it. These waters are the deserts of the sea.

The rich cold oceans

Green oceans are usually rich oceans, particularly if they are green far from land, where sediments could not possibly be coloring them. The richest are the Arctic and Antarctic Oceans, especially the Antarctic, which is the larger by far. The twelve million square miles of the Antarctic Ocean are richer in life than any other oceanic area of a similar extent.

Under the steady drive of the westerly winds, the surface waters of the Antarctic Ocean move continually eastward as the West Wind Drift, round and round the Antarctic region. The whole Antarctic area in fact forms an enormous single habitat for life, all of which is essentially marine, including the sea birds and sea mammals that use the margin of the icy land to rest and breed. This is the world not only of the albatross but of penguins and seals, and whales of all kinds, where there is more room at the top, so to speak, than anywhere else on earth. The great abundance of the highest forms of life reflects a much greater abundance at the base, and we can thus see in this Antarctic community an exceptionally clear example of how a pyramid of life is constructed.

This picture was taken in the Aleutian Islands, off the coast of Alaska. Although the land is barren, the icy water is opaque and green—thick with plant life, the basic foodstuff of the sea.

Lush sea pastures in the Antarctic

The life of the Antarctic Ocean begins, as it does elsewhere in the sunlit waters of the surface, with the diatoms and dinoflagellates, in this case especially with the diatoms. This sea pasture is so dense that no amount of animal consumption seems to affect it seriously, and the fertilizer salts are in such supply that they are never exhausted. Only the long night of winter calls a halt to the phytoplankton growth.

The Antarctic water is somewhat like a dilute but inexhaustible broth for the nourishment of life. Many varieties of small animals consume the diatoms forming the nutritious base of the broth, but one kind predominates above all others. This is the group of free-swimming shrimplike crustaceans we have already encountered as balloonists in the ocean currents. By far the most important is the creature known as *krill*, a name given it by Norwegian whalers. It occupies the place that the *Calanus* copepod occupies in the northern seas, although the krill is considerably larger, up to two and a half inches long. In fact, krill are about as large as an animal can become and still be able to gather microscopic diatoms as food. Resembling small lobsters, though without the claws, they swim by means of five pairs of paddles beneath the abdomen and trap plankton with the feathery appendages of the foreparts of their bodies. Throughout the

These petrels in the Antarctic Ocean are feeding on krill, which in turn feed on the almost limitless phytoplankton found here. Wherever you see ocean birds in abundance, you can be sure that the water is filled with life.

Antarctic Ocean they convert vegetation into meat to a greater extent than all other creatures of the plankton combined, although the copepods also do their part.

Such small crustaceans in the upper layers of the Antarctic Ocean are the natural food of many higher forms of life. The exceptionally abundant fish and squid are eaten by certain kinds of seals all around the edge of the Antarctic region. The food chain is similar to those we have already seen, but some of the creatures forming the links are different. Nevertheless the krill, though based on the exceptional richness of the diatom pasture of these waters, remain the key to the astonishing diversity and numbers of the larger Antarctic animals. This situation is in part the result of the super-abundance of krill, so great that only a small proportion is taken as food by other creatures, and is in part the result of the relatively large size of these crustaceans.

Most planktonic crustaceans, even a comparatively large copepod such as *Calanus*, are so small that they are taken as food mostly by creatures that are none too big themselves, such as the smaller jellyfish and fish. The size of the krill makes it possible for much larger animals to feed on them: they are big enough to be seen and captured one at a time by fish and sea birds that cannot see or capture individual copepods. The krill, in other words, serve as larger packages of meat.

THE PUZZLING
WEDDELL SEAL

One of Antarctica's most unusual inhabitants is the Weddell seal, a ten-foot, half-ton creature that thrives in the world's coldest waters. What special body adaptations let the Weddells survive here? How do the seals locate the fish, squid, and bottom invertebrates they feed on—often in total darkness and at depths as great as fifteen hundred feet? How do they find their way back to their vital breathing holes in the six-foot-thick surface ice? Can the seals "talk" to each other?

Scientists from the New York Zoological Society and the Woods Hole Oceanographic Institution found answers to some of these questions by setting up shop at the edge of the Antarctic Ocean and studying these fascinating animals, in and out of the water, for five weeks.

A Weddell seal comes up for air at a breathing hole in the ice, after a dive that may have lasted half an hour. The seal locates these holes by sonarlike sound echoes, which may also play a part in food location during the long Antarctic night. Apparently seals "talk" to each other, too, in the manner of dolphins. Weddells are capable of a surprising variety of underwater sounds.

Heavy neoprene-foam diving suits and this specially designed "SOC" (sub-ice observation chamber) allow researchers to watch and photograph seals while underwater sound equipment records the animals' voices. The water temperature is 28.6 degrees Fahrenheit, more than three degrees below the freezing point of fresh water.

Weddell seals show no discomfort in water cold enough to kill an unprotected human in a matter of minutes. At least three special body mechanisms help keep the seals warm: a thick layer of insulating blubber; a very high metabolism that "burns" food more than twice as fast as does that of land animals of similar size; and a remarkable ability to reduce the blood flow to the surface tissues, where body heat is most quickly lost to the surrounding water or air.

The pyramid of life

In a typical food chain the size of the animals increases from one link or step to the next. There is safety in being large. The larger the animal, the more difficult it becomes for some other creature to devour it. At the same time it becomes more difficult for the animal to obtain enough food. This is one of the reasons why there are fewer animals at the end of the chain than there are nearer the beginning. Another reason is that the animals at the end of the chain use up a great deal of energy just staying alive and use only a small fraction of what they eat for growth and reproduction. If they are warm-blooded animals, such as birds and mammals, they tend to lose heat rapidly to the cold surrounding water. And if they must swim vigorously to capture food, thereby expending a great deal of energy in movement, they use even more of their food for maintenance and even less for growth and reproduction.

This situation can be compared to a pyramid. In spite of their enormous size, the animals at the top of the pyramid are relatively few in number compared with those lower down, and their total weight is very much less. Roughly speaking, a thousand pounds of diatoms, which is an unimaginable number of individual diatoms, make about a hundred pounds of animal plankton such as copepods or krill, which in turn make only ten pounds of fish, and finally but one pound of seal. At every level in the pyramid about nine-tenths of the food value is lost as energy or heat, and only one-tenth passes on to the next level.

Despite its name, the Antarctic crabeater seal does not eat crabs. It feeds on krill, the crustacean that also supports the giant baleen whales. The crabeater's krill-eating technique is not unlike that of the whales: it takes in a mouthful of the crustaceans and water, forces the water out between specially interlocking side teeth, and then swallows the krill.

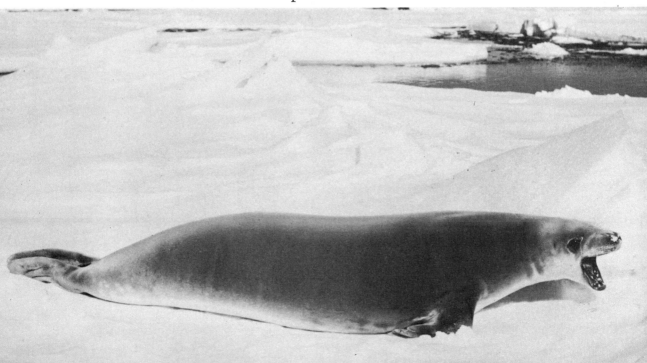

Thus we see that half a ton of diatoms is necessary for one pound of growth of a seal and also for every pound of baby seal that a mother seal produces. And the seal may not be at the top of the pyramid, for seals are hunted in their turn by killer whales, the most ferocious animals in the ocean. The same relationship holds, however, and for every new pound that a killer whale adds to its weight, it must consume ten pounds of seal. No wonder this kind of whale is not more numerous than it is. Each pound of killer whale actually represents five tons of diatoms and other vegetation of the ocean pasture. The pyramid of life in the sea, as elsewhere, is very broad at the base, but the top may be very small, depending on how many steps it takes to get there. As we have seen, each level is only one-tenth as large as the one below it.

Clearly there are advantages to being near the base of the pyramid. Baleen whales, for example, feed directly on krill, and so they are only one step removed from feeding on the vegetation itself. It takes only a hundred pounds of diatoms to make a pound of baleen whale. Giant whales are therefore both numerous and large: numerous because there is so much food available in the form of krill, and large because they waste comparatively little energy in obtaining it.

The leopard seal, another Antarctic species, is equipped with sharp fangs and a gullet adapted to taking in large chunks of food. It feeds on penguins and the young of other seals, placing it a step higher in the food pyramid than the crabeater seal. Leopard seals in turn are preyed upon by the killer whales at the top of the pyramid.

119

KILLER WHALE

WEDDELL SEAL

SQUID

ANTARCTIC FISH

KRILL

PLANT PLANKTON

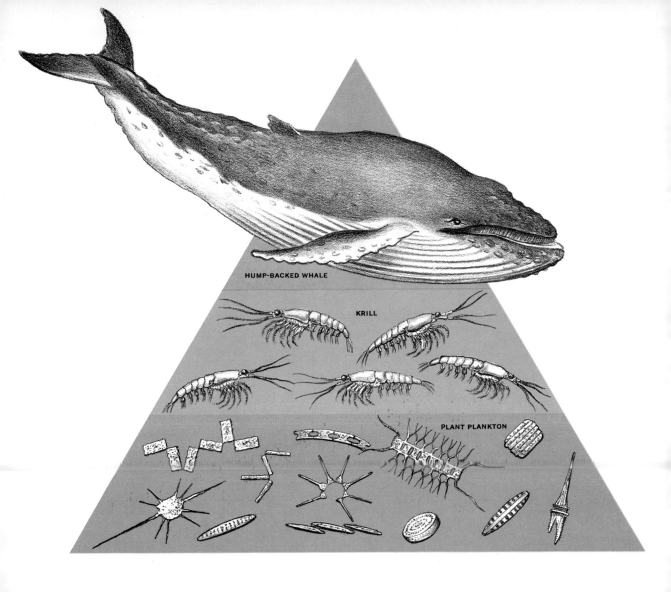

HUMP-BACKED WHALE

KRILL

PLANT PLANKTON

PYRAMIDS OF LIFE

All ocean life is based ultimately on the food produced by the phytoplankton and transferred upwards to progressively larger animals. Since nine-tenths of this food value is lost at each transfer, the process may be represented as a pyramid with large numbers of small organisms at the base and small numbers of the largest predators at the top. In the pyramid shown at the left, then, ten thousand pounds of diatoms can produce a thousand pounds of krill, which produce a hundred pounds of fish and squid, which in turn produce ten pounds of seal, which finally produce one pound of killer whale. By contrast, the giant baleen whales utilize the phytoplankton energy much more efficiently, by cutting out some of the intermediate steps and feeding directly on the krill, as shown in the pyramid above. Thus, while ten thousand pounds of diatoms are required to produce only one pound of killer whale, that same quantity of diatoms will produce a hundred pounds of baleen whale.

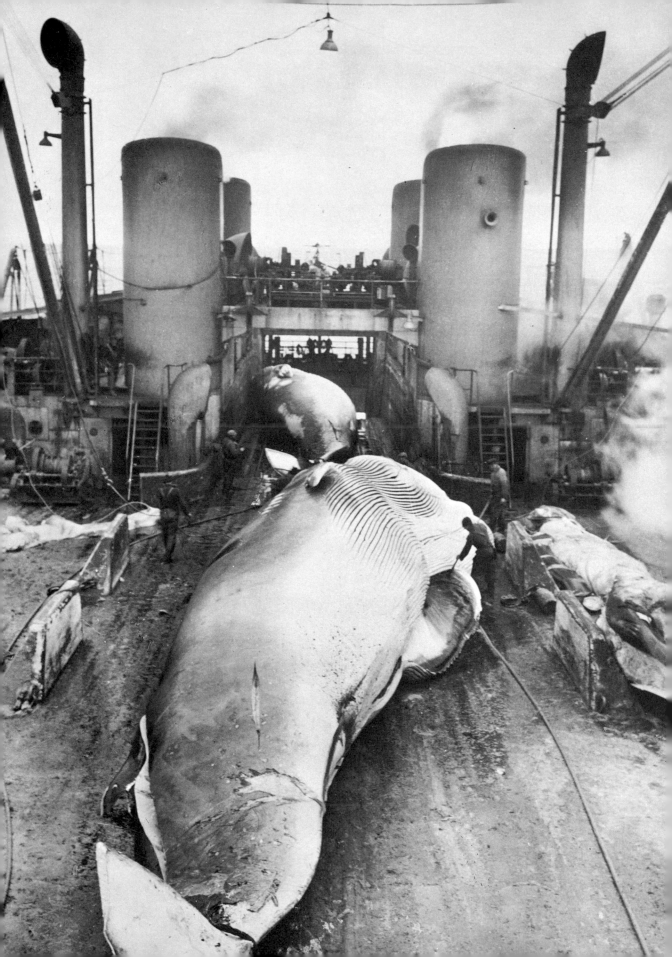

The world's largest animals

The baleen, or whalebone, whales are the largest creatures that have ever lived. The largest of them, the blue whale, or sulphur-bottomed whale, is three times as large as the biggest dinosaur that ever walked on land during the age of reptiles. Whalers have taken blue whales more than a hundred feet long and weighing 150 tons.

All such whales are equipped with mouth strainers instead of teeth, consisting of so-called whalebone, horny plates with fringed edges. The belly of a baleen whale is pleated, or fluted, from chin to navel. The pleats give its underside great flexibility and allow its mouth to hang down as a huge bag for scooping the seawater and whatever is floating or swimming in it. When the animal brings its jaws together, closing the bag, its tongue squeezes the water out between the fringed whalebone plates. The plankton of plants and small animals also passes through, but the krill are retained. Even a moderate-sized whale has been found to contain as much as three tons of freshly captured krill in its stomach. Blue whales have sieve plates three feet long; but the once nearly extinct Atlantic right whale has plates twelve feet long, with jaws to match, though the creature as a whole is somewhat smaller than the blue whale of the southern ocean.

As a rule the blue, fin-backed, and hump-backed whales, all of them whalebone whales, cruise slowly through the water, either singly or in herds. Speed, which they have in reserve, is not important unless they are under attack by whalers or by a pack of ravenous killer whales. Feeding on krill is a quiet business which rushing through the water would only make more difficult. The krill, unlike most of their close relatives, confine themselves to a thin zone within thirty feet of the surface, where the diatom growth is most dense. They swarm in shoals from a few square yards to nearly an acre in size. Sometimes these crustaceans are so densely packed that the water itself takes on their reddish color, and patches of various sizes may extend for hundreds of square miles. Over large areas of the Antarctic Ocean, in

In place of teeth, the baleen whales have long, thin strips of whalebone, or baleen, which are fringed along one edge and which hang down in a sheet from both sides of the upper jaw. When feeding, the whale gulps in an enormous mouthful of water and plankton; it then closes its mouth and lifts its tongue, forcing the water and smaller plankton out through the sievelike baleen sheets but retaining and then swallowing the larger plankton.

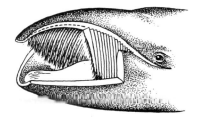

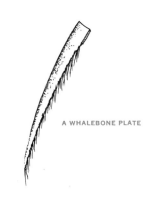

A WHALEBONE PLATE

The massive carcasses of two baleen whales sprawl on the deck of a whaling factory ship. Overhunting has dangerously reduced the numbers of several species of these giants.

This is the stomach of a blue whale, opened up to show its contents. Inside is three tons of krill, enough to make sixty pounds of whale flesh.

fact, the whales have no need to go in search of food; they simply browse on the krill, like cows in a meadow.

The large whalebone whales of the North Atlantic, North Pacific, and Arctic Oceans, which feed on swarms of *Calanus* instead of krill, were practically exterminated by whalers during the nineteenth century. The whalers then turned their attention to the Antarctic, and so we need to go back about fifty years to see how large the Antarctic whale population could be. At that time apparently about a half a million giant whales were present in the Antarctic waters, plowing gently through the sea within the limits of the krill. Since then about 350,000 blue whales have been killed, and both the blue whale and the much smaller hump-backed whale have been brought to near-extinction. Only the fin-backed whale remains in significant numbers, but at the rate at which it is being caught at present, this whale may soon join the ranks of the species in danger of extinction.

Small numbers of each kind may survive, however, for when whales are few and far between, it costs more to catch them than they are worth. The question is then whether small, scattered populations can continue to breed.

The breeding and raising of whales is a remarkable process. Even though fully marine, they are mammals: they have warm blood, they must surface to breathe air periodically, and they bear their young alive and suckle them for a time. Yet the far-southern part of the Antarctic Ocean is unsuitable for an event that takes so long, for the Antarctic, like the Arctic, has its seasons. The rich diatom pasture and the abundant krill that feed on it are features of the long, bright Antarctic spring and summer. When winter approaches and daylight grows dim and disappears, diatom growth ceases and the krill also disappear, at least from the surface waters. How many whales spend the winter there is not known, but certainly it is no place for bearing and nursing young. So at the end of the Antarctic summer the whales migrate north into warmer waters to bear their young. Until they return to the south again the following spring, they do not feed but seemingly live on the reserves of fat built up during the six-month-long banquet of the previous season.

Newborn whales have very little blubber and would probably quickly freeze to death if born in the icy waters of the polar seas. As it is, they grow very fast on the extremely

One of the baleen sheets shows clearly in this dead blue whale, lying on its back aboard a factory ship. The baleen whales belong to a scientific group called the Mysticeti, meaning "mustache whales"—a reference to the appearance of the fringed baleen plates. Once in heavy demand as the raw material of stays for old-fashioned corsets, baleen today is mostly ground into bone meal, an ingredient in fertilizers and animal feed.

fattening whale milk supplied by the mother. Young blue whales gain as much as two hundred pounds a day, thus ranking as the fastest-growing animals in the world as well as the largest. At birth a blue whale is about twenty-three feet long and weighs from two to three tons. Seven months later, when it is weaned from its mother's milk, it weighs about twenty-three tons; and at a year and a half it is more than sixty feet long and forty tons in weight. For the remainder of its growth period, until it is five years old, it grows by ninety pounds a day. This is quite a remarkable performance when we consider that the diet of both mother and young, except for the nursing, consists of tiny crustaceans consumed at the rate of about two tons a day.

A sea of penguins

The Antarctic Ocean is as much a sea of birds as it is of whales. The krill offer a sumptuous repast to all who can take them, partly because they swarm in such dense masses and partly because they live their adult life so close to the surface, at least during the Antarctic day. How they live through the dark winter is not known, although their red color suggests that deeper water may well be their proper home. This is where the young krill are found even in summer, having descended from the surface to a deeper current that carries them south to the edge of the continental ice, where they come to the surface again. And it is here, all

Thoroughly at home in a climate that humans find the most inhospitable on earth, Adélie penguins congregate in great numbers all around the edge of the Antarctic continent. Population counts have shown that a single 500-acre Adélie rookery may contain half a million birds.

around the margin of the Antarctic region, that the hosts of penguins and other sea birds make their homes, dividing their time between fishing at sea and resting or breeding on the ice and rocks along the shore.

More so than any other bird, penguins are oceanic creatures, as well adapted to living in the sea as the porpoise or whale, and just as warm-blooded and air-breathing. Like all birds, though, they must lay and hatch eggs on land. There they are amusing figures as they waddle along with an upright stance, looking like small people in formal dress, yet in the sea they are the most agile of all birds capable of swimming underwater.

A penguin's padded body is streamlined for speed; its wings are hard and firm for beating against water instead of air; its chest muscles and keel are heavy and strong; its feathers are modified to provide a dry insulating coat. The bird is as fitted to the water as any porpoise, fish, or squid— a lithe, darting, efficient animal with eyes well suited for seeing through water. It needs only an occasional fast flip to the surface to get air, and even that is as brief as the jump of a fish. It progresses by porpoising, traveling below the surface for ten to thirty yards and then shooting into the air in an arc of seven or eight feet, to vanish again with hardly a ripple.

Penguins feed mostly on krill, although they welcome fish and squid as well. They like krill so much that they will gobble them until they are well distended, and then like the ancient Romans at a banquet, vomit and start all over.

There are several kinds of penguins that exploit the Antarctic wealth in a variety of ways. The best known, the emperor and Adélie penguins, fringe the entire Antarctic shore; the kings, gentoos, and rock hoppers hold the barren islands of the West Wind Drift, the same islands on which the wandering and sooty albatrosses nest; others have their land stations along the shores of South America wherever the sea is cold and full of fish and shrimp. But only the three-and-a-half-foot-tall emperor, the largest of all penguins, endures the terrible cold of the Antarctic winter, cuddling and hatching its eggs on the edge of the Great Ice Barrier during the months-long night.

The emperor penguin is the only bird that endures the rigors of the long Antarctic winter. Here we see three adult emperors and a number of the communally raised young.

The Antarctic upwelling

The immense and never-ceasing fertility of the Antarctic waters results from a continual upwelling of minerals from below, rather than from a mixing of surface and deeper layers by spring and autumn storms. As elsewhere in the oceans, the bottom layers are rich in fertilizer salts because such salts are continually being added to the deeper water by the decaying bodies of plankton and other organisms sinking from overhead. These salts accumulate in the dark depths, since they can be utilized only by plant life in the presence of sunlight. Close around the Antarctic region, with its massive icy covering, the sea becomes exceptionally chilled. This cold water is very heavy because in addition to being cooled to polar temperatures, it is given an extra burden of salt, for the ice forming at its surface throws out salts in the process of freezing. The heavy water consequently sinks to the sea floor and moves away to the north from the continental shelf.

At the same time, farther out to sea, another sort of water mass is forming. Diluted by heavy rains and snowfall together with ice melted in summer, the water becomes relatively light and drifts northward on the surface. With all this water moving north, other water must come in to take its place. Moving down from the north, a deep mass of water, rich in fertilizer salts, rides to the surface over the

The tremendous fertility of the south polar seas is the result of a phenomenon called the Antarctic upwelling. In the bitter Antarctic winter, an extremely cold, salty mass of water forms in the area. This dense water slides down the continental slope and heads northward along the very bottom of the ocean. At the same time, another body of cold water, made light by the addition of fresh water from melting ice and snow, also heads northward, but at the surface. These two northbound masses of water, one at the bottom and one at the surface, must be replaced by the water sandwiched between them. This middle layer of water is drawn southward from thousands of miles to the north, and in its journey it has become rich in minerals derived from decaying organic matter sinking from above. The upwelling of this mineral-laden water to the surface, where sunlight is also available, triggers the prodigious bloom of phytoplankton in the Antarctic Ocean.

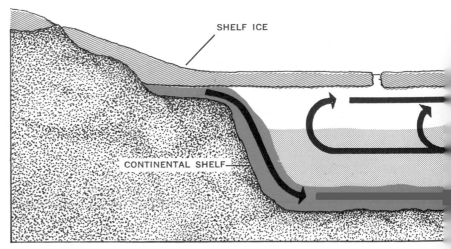

SHELF ICE

CONTINENTAL SHELF

water sinking down from the Antarctic continental shelf. In this way a tremendous upwelling of rich water occurs in the Antarctic throughout the year.

Currents such as these are far larger and much slower than those produced at the surface by prevailing winds. They are known as convection currents, and they are responsible for the nature of the ocean at depths below which light does not reach. By carrying oxygen down to the sea floor in the greatest depths, they make it possible for animals to live there. And they are responsible for the remarkable coldness of the deeper layers of the ocean even under the equator.

The replacement water reaching the Antarctic, with its load of fertilizer salts, has moved all the way from the North Atlantic and across the oceanic abyss, finally to rise toward the surface again in the far-southern ocean. Arctic and Antarctic cold reach far into the opposite hemispheres by traveling beneath the warmer surface layers of temperate and tropical latitudes, but so slowly that several thousand years may be necessary to make the entire journey. For instance, one analysis of deep-ocean water taken from the middle of the North Atlantic Ocean showed that it began to sink from the surface in the Arctic over a thousand years ago. In all the time that has passed since the Norman invasion of Britain, the water apparently has moved only part of the way to the equator.

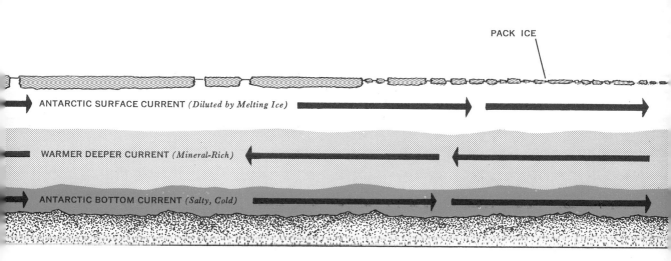

PACK ICE

ANTARCTIC SURFACE CURRENT *(Diluted by Melting Ice)*

WARMER DEEPER CURRENT *(Mineral-Rich)*

ANTARCTIC BOTTOM CURRENT *(Salty, Cold)*

The Humboldt Current

As the great west winds drive the southern ocean around Antarctica to make the West Wind Drift, the southern end of South America diverts part of the cold current, forcing it northward as a steady flow known as the Humboldt, or Peruvian, Current. It moves north as a broad band of water several hundred miles wide all along the western coast of the continent; when it is close to the equator, it swings west to become part of the South Equatorial Current heading for the far-western part of the Pacific. In fact, it serves as the eastern portion of the great revolving current system of the South Pacific Ocean.

The thirty- to forty-mile-wide inshore part of the Humboldt Current supports one of the richest populations in the world. This is where the water is coldest, and the cool current flowing north alongside the warm tropical coast all the way to Peru and Ecuador creates a constant haze. The whole inshore stretch of the current presents a most remarkable picture, for it combines the features of a current rip along the outer edge of the cooler water with the general abundance of life that we saw in the Antarctic, although mostly with different characters playing the various parts.

The sea pasture is there in all its richness, but in addition to the diatoms, luminescent dinoflagellates play a greater role. In place of krill, the chief consumers of this pasturage are copepods and small opossum shrimp. Finally, at the top of the pyramid are birds instead of whales, although groups of hump-backed whales are fairly common. Within the narrow belt of the Humboldt Current along the coast, copepods, shrimp, small jellyfish, salps, and other planktonic creatures are so dense in places as to make the water seem like a thick soup. The farther west you go, the less ocean life you see, and eventually the ocean becomes as barren as it can be.

Every naturalist who has seen the teeming life of the Humboldt Current has marveled at it. According to one of them, the normally blue-green waters often become great red seas colored by myriads of microscopic dinoflagellates;

The Humboldt Current, named for a nineteenth-century German naturalist and pioneer oceanographer, arises from the West Wind Drift, moves northward along the western coast of South America, and ultimately is turned west to become the South Equatorial Current. The cold, mineral-laden waters of the Humboldt Current are among the most fertile in all the world's oceans.

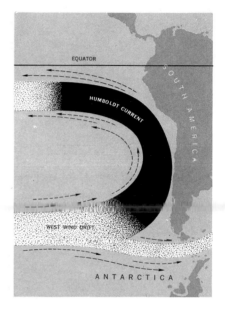

Peruvian boobies, second only to cormorants as guano producers, divide their time between tending their nests and fishing for anchovies in the rich Humboldt Current off the coast of Peru.

CORMORANTS
AND BOOBIES

ANCHOVIES

DIATOMS AND
DINOFLAGELLATES

The cold, rich waters of the Humboldt Current support a food pyramid in which cormorants and boobies feed upon anchovies, which in turn feed upon the teeming phytoplankton. A hundred pounds of phytoplankton, consumed by ten pounds of anchovies, will produce one pound of bird.

sometimes great areas of the surface are reddened by the vast numbers of small lobsterlike crustaceans, which are important as food for the fishes and for the fishermen birds. More striking still are the immense schools of small fishes, the anchovies, which are followed by bonitos and other fishes and are preyed on by flocks of cormorants, pelicans, boobies, and other sea birds. The calm sea itself is often ruffled with shimmering areas where myriads of anchovies are moving near the surface, using their gill rakers to strain out the invisible plant life that thickens the water.

Clouds of birds

The birds are dominant; and the long files of pelicans, the low-moving black clouds of cormorants, and the rain of plunging boobies are unequaled anywhere else in the world. Another naturalist described countless numbers of sea birds fishing in dense, excited flocks, passing in endless files from one fishing ground to another, or massed in great rafts on the sea; sinuous files of birds moving through the air in repeated curves lost in the distance, while over the water processions passed rapidly, steadily, hour after hour, with rarely a break in their ranks during the entire day. Cormorants fished from the surface in a sea of small fry, swimming, diving, and gobbling until they could hold no more. Boobies fished from the air, plunging into the water in endless cataracts; then would come a mass of foam from which hundreds of fishers took wing at a low angle to return to the throng above and dive again. Most astonishing was the instantaneous disappearance from the air of flocks of up to a thousand boobies when they happened to pass over a school of fish. As one bird, they plunged seaward, and the sky suddenly became empty.

So here is the pyramid of life again, with its base of microscopic diatoms and dinoflagellates and its peak in feathered glory. But this time there are only three levels: diatoms, anchovies, and birds. In an almost literal sense the sea birds skim the cream off the top, but as fast as they take it, it is renewed from below. The birds are mostly tropical, yet the cool water of the Antarctic flows almost to the equator, and from the coast of southern Chile to the coast of northern Peru the Peruvian penguin feeds on the abundant anchovies with all the rest.

134

Why does all this rich life thrive inside the Humboldt Current nearest the coast? It is not derived from the surface water diverted north from the West Wind Drift; for if this were so, the whole of the Humboldt Current, not just its eastern margin, would hold a wealth of life. The explanation lies as much in the wind as in the sea; wind as well as water flows up from the southern ocean. The south wind blows quietly along the coast almost to the equator and continually blows the inshore surface water of the ocean out to sea. This out-blown water has to be replaced by water that can come only from the ocean depths. And since the coast itself is where the high, steep range of the Andes slips down into the deep Pacific Ocean, with no continental shelf to interrupt its plunge, the replacement water welling upward comes from depths that are cold, dark, and rich in nutrient salts. As long as the wind blows from the south, the offshore movement of the ocean surface goes on, and the upwelling continues. And as long as the upwelling continues, the water remains cold and rich, and the spectacular abundance of life persists.

From man's point of view, these Peruvian cormorants (shown with a scattering of brown pelicans) are the most valuable birds in the world. A single bird colony may consume a thousand tons of fish each day, converting much of it into the finest of natural fertilizers.

Red tides

A grim windrow of dead fish marks the border of a red tide. But nothing is ever really lost from the sea: the nourishment these creatures had taken from the waters will now return to the base of the great pyramid of life, part of the perpetual replenishment of the bountiful ocean.

For reasons not understood, the south wind ceases once every few years, and a wind from the north, *El Niño*, moves down. This is catastrophic. When the south wind gives way to the north, the inshore waters no longer move out, the upwelling stops, and the sea temperatures steadily rise. Then all the life normally associated with the cool Humboldt Current water begins to die. The characteristic diatoms and dinoflagellates disappear, and "red tides" of other kinds, some of them poisonous, take their place. High temperature, stagnant water, and strange plant life take their toll, and the sea becomes a graveyard for the fish and crustaceans that were teeming a short while before. The sea birds panic, abandon their fledglings, and either strike out blindly to the north or south or fly excitedly in circles, only to die of star-

vation on the beaches. When it is over, the bird population may be reduced from its usual thirty million to eight or five million. The water reeks of the hydrogen sulfide of decaying bodies and blackens the paint of ships.

Then, as the old life goes, new kinds of sea life move down with the wind and current from the north. Thousands upon thousands of hammerhead sharks have been seen to invade the southern waters, traveling together as an army a couple of miles wide and of indefinite length. They are accompanied by jumping giant manta rays and by schools of large flying fish that are pursued by equally tropical dolphin fish. Overhead come flocks of sea birds, more tropical than those that had been there before. Then once more the south wind blows, and the current cools and moves northward again. The invaders retreat, and the old order slowly becomes reestablished.

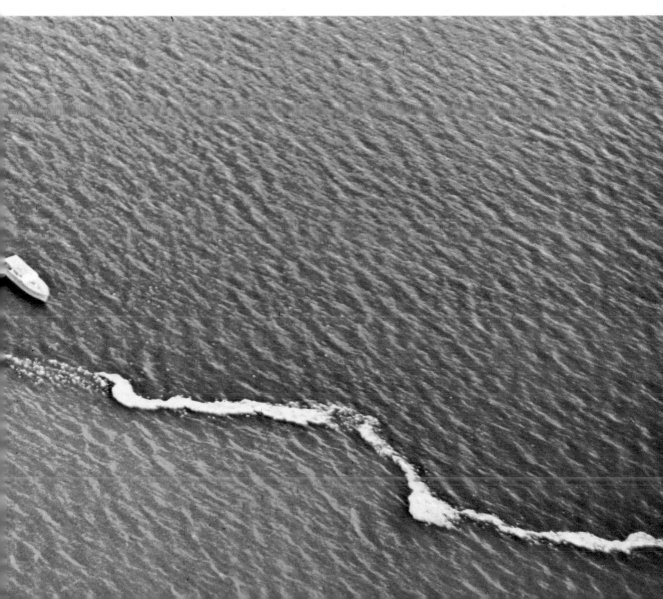

The

Ocean Floor

The floor of the ocean begins at the edge of the tide. Although the rocks and beaches of the seashore are considered part of the floor, the pounding of the surf and the daily exposures to sun and air create special problems for plants and animals that live there. Beyond the low-tide mark, waves still churn the sand and swirl against the rocks; but a little farther out where the water is somewhat deeper, the sea floor becomes a much calmer place, even though storms break overhead. From here out to the edge of the continental shelf, which may be anywhere from a few miles to several hundred miles away from the shore, the floor of the sea is fairly flat. This is the platform where most of the animal life of the ocean floor is to be found. It is not shallow, to be sure, but even out near the far edge of the continental shelf the depth of the water seldom exceeds five or six hundred feet.

If you were to enter the sea from a sandy beach at low tide and move outward to explore the floor of the sea, the bottom would gradually change to shell gravel and finally to mud as the depth of water became greater. The currents would become gentler, and the light would grow steadily weaker until only a murky, faint greenish light remained. However, off rocky shores, such as the Atlantic coast north of Cape Cod and almost the entire length of the Pacific coast, seaweeds find anchorage to such an extent that they form submarine forests that shelter and support a host of living creatures.

Forests of seaweed require light just as much as do the microscopic plants of the open ocean, and they are therefore restricted to the margin of the sea where water is shallow and a rocky floor is close to the surface. Often, at exceptionally low tides, such a belt of seaweed will be temporarily exposed; but as a rule weeds of this sort, namely, the great brown kelps, remain submerged or at least awash. All such kelp beds inhabit only the cooler seas of the Northern and Southern Hemispheres. How far out from shore they can live depends on how long and how strong a stalk they can grow between the holdfast on the rock below and the surface layer of water where the large brown blades carry on their plant activity.

Forests of kelp

The youthful Charles Darwin saw the largest kelp in the world as the *Beagle* sailed through the narrow Strait of Magellan. In his own words, they were:

> . . . great brown blades [fifty feet long] growing from inch-thick stems a hundred and more feet below the surface. Almost every blade is so thickly incrusted with corallines as to be of a white color. We find exquisitely delicate structures, some inhabited by simple hydra-like polyps, others by more organized kinds, and beautiful compound ascidians. On the flat surface various limpets, whelks, sea slugs and some bivalves are attached. Innumerable crustacea frequent every part of the plant. On shaking the great entangled roots, a pile of small fish, shells, cuttle fish, crabs of all orders, sea eggs, starfish, beautiful holothurians, planarians

Laminaria is a typical member of the kelps, a group of brown algae found along rocky shores. It can grow to a length of fifteen to twenty feet, though it is usually much smaller.

and crawling worms of a multitude of forms, all fall out together. . . . I can only compare these great aquatic forests of the southern hemisphere with the terrestrial ones of the inter-tropical regions. Amidst blades of this plant numerous species of fish live which no where else would find food or shelter; with their destruction the many cormorants, divers, and other fishing birds, the otters, seals, and porpoises would soon perish also.

Here is the web of life in all its rich complexity, with a sea-weed as its base and everything struggling for a place on or among the blades.

Elsewhere kelp forests are less spectacular but are none-theless important as living communities. Delicate traceries of calcareous sea mats encrust both blade and stem, as do colonial ascidians, or sea squirts, including the golden star *Botryllus*. Colonies of hydroids attached by slender stalks produce and liberate minute jellyfish that swim out in the open sea. Not least among the creatures clinging to the smooth brown blades of kelp are the stalked jellyfish that are permanently anchored by a slender stalk and capture their food in the manner of sea anemones. Small whelks and colorful sea slugs browse on all these creatures—on sea mats, sea squirts, and hydroids.

A variety of sea creatures, including tiny barnacles and inch-wide anemones, cling to stems near the floor of the kelp forest. Skin divers must exercise caution in exploring kelp beds, because it is easy to become dangerously entangled in the tough, sinuous algae.

At the base of the weeds are sponges, worms, brittle stars, red and yellow starfish, mussels, and clams, all sheltered among the tangled holdfasts of closely neighboring kelps. Among the stalks and blades swirling gently with the currents swim small fish and many kinds of shrimp, for the junglelike kelp bed affords shelter from fish too large to swim in the watery maze. It is a nursery for young creatures that are still too small to fend for themselves in a more exposed place. All along the rock-bound Atlantic coast from Maine to Labrador, and around the rocky coasts of Northern Europe, young lobsters settle and grow to maturity on the sea floor among the kelp and rocks. Only when grown do they move into deeper water farther from the shore, with regular inshore and offshore migration as summers and winters interchange.

Great kelp beds abound along the cold-water coasts of the North Pacific, from the islands of Japan across the arc of the Aleutians to Alaska, and south along the western coast to central California. Here the story is much the same except that the kelp is bigger and many of the characters are different. The sea swirls among the rocks, and in the few seconds between the ebb and the inrush of a wave you can sometimes see the great green anemone, a solitary surf-loving jewel of the sea that may be thirty inches in circumference. Then the kelp begins, and there lives the abalone.

The abalone, a large sea snail named *Haliotis*, with its famous mother-of-pearl ear-shaped shell, is a vegetarian that spends its life crawling among the sea forest and stuffing itself continually on green sea lettuce and brown kelp. It clings so tightly to rocks with its muscular foot that a crowbar is needed to lift it off once it is alarmed. Green and purple sea urchins, vegetarians also, live abundantly on the sea floor among the kelp; and spiny clawless lobsters take the place of the eastern kind, though both, in company with hermit crabs, are thoroughgoing scavengers.

The eight-inch garibaldi is one of the kelp forest's most colorful and common fish. Garibaldis are short-tempered and quarrelsome among themselves, each fish staking out a definite territory and jealously driving off all trespassers. The eggs are laid in nests and are fiercely guarded; even a human swimmer is liable to get a frightening (but harmless) nip if he ventures too close to the nesting site.

Sea otters

Some of the most interesting inhabitants of the west-coast kelp are the sea otters. These mammals are true creatures of the Pacific kelp, for they can live nowhere else. A few decades ago their fur was fashionable for ladies' coats, and they had been brought to the verge of extinction, with only a few left among the cold islands of the Aleutian chain. Now, after about fifty years of complete protection against hunters, sea otters are coming back and can be seen again as far south as central California.

If you should see one, off Point Lobos or thereabouts, you will probably see several, all with their front paws crossed on their chests, tails out, webbed toes up, floating on their backs and cat-napping in the water, often with a blade of kelp twisted about their bodies that keeps them from drifting onto any nearby rocks while they sleep. The kelp forest not only contains their food and serves as a breakwater against the sweep of waves but screens them from the killer whales, their only enemy aside from man.

Three times a day—morning, noon, and evening—otters dive to the bottom to get their food, descending silently without a splash and kicking powerfully with their huge

The California sea otter is thoroughly adapted to life in the water, and rarely if ever comes ashore. It spends its life in the kelp, as far as thirty miles out to sea. An expert diver, the sea otter forages for food on the floor of the kelp forest in water up to three hundred feet deep.

hind paddles, their front paws folded over their chests. On the murky sea floor perhaps a hundred feet below, among the rocks at the base of the kelp, they take crabs, sea urchins, snails, and clams, and somehow manage to pull the red abalone from its anchorage. Then they surface again to feed, for sea otters are as air-breathing as seals or porpoises. If a sea otter comes up with a clam, it also brings up a flat stone and, while floating on its back, smashes the bivalve against it. If it brings up a sea urchin, it bites a hole in the shell and sucks out the soft parts inside.

Sea otters remain among the kelp even when bearing and nursing their young. Seals, sea lions, and sea elephants are equally adept at getting a living from coastal seas, but they must come ashore to bear their offspring.

The magnificent coral reefs

In the warmer waters of tropical and semitropical seas there are none of the dense seaweed beds so typical of the more

Using its chest for a dinner table, this sea otter settles down to a meal of clams in the quiet water at the base of a rock cliff. If you want to see these rare animals, you must seek them in their natural habitat—no zoo or aquarium in the world owns a California sea otter.

115

A formation of massive elkhorn coral marks the entrance to the ocean's most enchanting wonderland—the coral reef. Nowhere else in nature, either in the sea or on dry land, have so much beauty and variety of life been crowded into so small an area. Every square foot of the reef holds new surprises to dazzle the eye and delight the mind. Happily for man, coral flourishes in warm, shallow, well-lighted waters, making the reef world relatively easy for the diver to enter and enjoy. But for all its gemlike beauty, the coral reef is not without dangers, and the human who enters it must never forget that he is only a visitor, an outsider who must accept the reef on its own terms or suffer harsh consequences. Is it worth the risk? Yes. No man ever visited a coral reef without longing to return again and again.

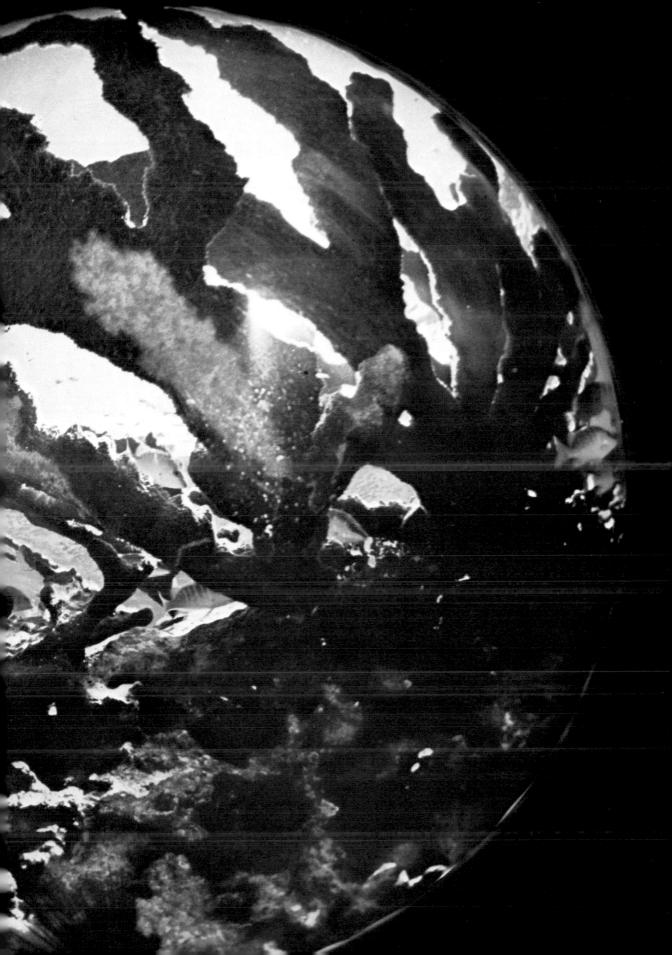

northerly and more southerly oceans, except for floating weeds such as those of the Sargasso Sea. Conditions favoring such luxuriant vegetative growth are not present. In place of the seaweeds, however, you find the stony jungles of coral reef supporting an equally rich community.

Although corals are animals, a reef of living coral is truly a sea garden. Not only are the stony corals themselves many-colored, with violet and brown, pink, white, green, scarlet, and yellow polyps making up the colonies, but equally vivid and beautifully shaped organisms live among them.

The coral animal is closely related to the sea anemone of the tide pools. It can exist in reef-producing masses only so long as food, oxygen, and light reach it in abundance. Such conditions are fully met only in shallow water in the warmer regions of the ocean.

Each little coral cup resembles a stony sea anemone enveloped in a somewhat transparent but colorful veil of living tissue. It reaches with its ring of tentacles for sustenance in the swirling waters in which it lives. New cups grow from the sides of older ones, forming great coral creations. Among them are the large branching staghorn corals, the compact boulders of brain coral, and many other forms. All are likely to be surmounted by various kinds of soft corals lacking limy skeletons, such as sea fans and sea rods, among whose

The living coral animals retreat into their limy skeletons at low tide, unable to bear exposure to the air and to the heat of the sun. But a dazzling variety of sea creatures lurk in the labyrinth of pools and passageways among the shelflike coral formations.

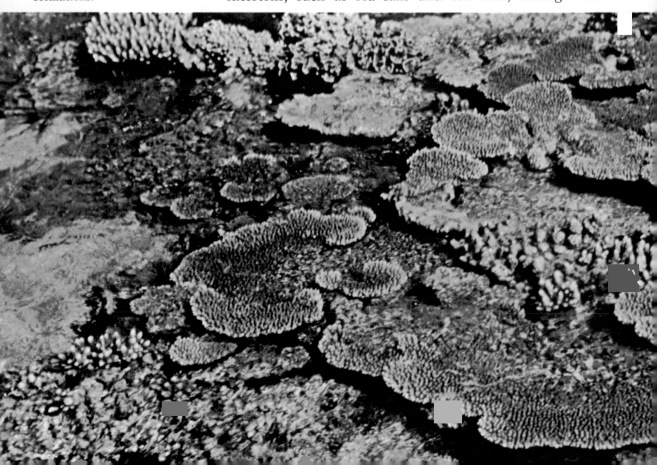

branches dart brilliantly colored, astonishingly beautiful coral-reef fish.

Coral's partnership with plants

Part of the coral's secret of survival lies in its partnership with plants. Indeed, coral requires strong sunlight, not for itself but for its partners. Coral tissue, like that of many sea anemones and some other creatures, is filled with a multitude of microscopic living plants. These plant cells have finally been identified as certain kinds of dinoflagellates, similar to, and probably identical with, the unarmored dinoflagellates of plankton.

Within the coral tissue the plant cells and the coral animal cells work together in harmony. So long as sufficient light is available, the plant cells grow and multiply, nourished by the carbon dioxide and nutrient salts furnished by the animal tissue. On the other hand, the animal tissue not only receives the abundant oxygen that is a by-product of plant photosynthesis, but actually receives as a bonus large amounts of surplus carbohydrates manufactured by the plants. Without the plants' help, corals would smother in the congested masses that compose a reef. Even as it is, the inner slopes of coral reefs are dead or dying.

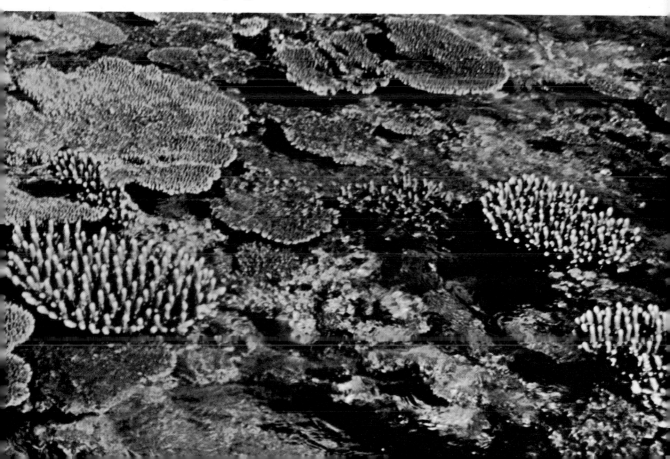

THE COLORFUL CORALS

Among the most beautiful and varied of nature's creations are the corals, which flourish throughout the world wherever the conditions of water, light, and temperature are favorable. Shown here (*left to right*) are the polyps, or living portions, of four representative varieties: *Mycedium*, from the Red Sea; an unidentified species, also from the Red Sea; *Goniopora*, commonly called daisy coral, from New Caledonia; and a brain coral from the Bahamas. Each specimen is shown here about three-quarters life size. Some coral varieties, including *Mycedium*, exhibit even more spectacular colors when viewed under ultraviolet light.

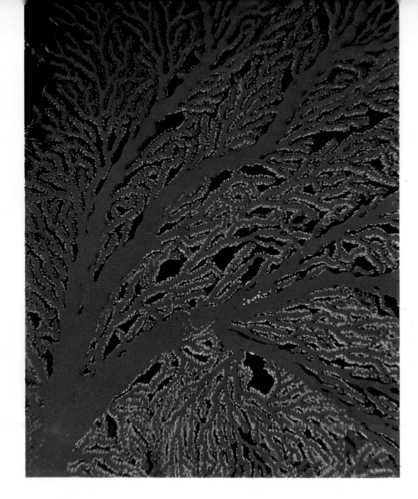

In place of the limy skeletons of the rocklike corals, the sea fans (*left and right*) produce a tough, horny substance that gives them a certain amount of resiliency. The broad face of each fan (which may be a foot or more across) is presented to the prevailing current, so that the polyps lining each branch and twig will encounter a maximum number of food organisms.

Where corals flourish

The corals of a reef actually require far more food than is supplied by plant cells living within their own tissues. Only on the rough seaward edge of a reef do the corals maintain their own kingdom, forever growing out against the force of the waves that bring them their food and wash away the clogging debris. Moreover, live coral reefs, as distinct from isolated corals or coral patches, flourish only where the sea temperature exceeds 70 degrees Fahrenheit throughout the year. Even in the tropics the sea is too cold for coral to survive if cold water wells up to the surface, as it does occasionally in the Humboldt Current and in the somewhat similar Benguela Current off the west coast of Africa.

Within the tropical ocean itself the growth of reef-forming corals varies according to the latitude and temperature. The spectacular branching kinds of coral flourish only where the sea temperature remains above 75 degrees; the bordering regions to the north and south of this rather narrow equa-

152

torial zone contain mainly the more resistant but less spectacular encrusting kinds of coral, together with the rounder nonbranching types such as brain coral and fungus coral.

Sensitivity to even moderately cool water therefore limits coral reefs to a belt around the earth in latitudes between 30 degrees north and 30 degrees south of the equator. In this region they are to be found everywhere but on the western shores of the continents. One such reef far excels the rest. This is the Great Barrier Reef, which extends practically unbroken for 1250 miles from New Guinea southward along the entire northeastern coast of Australia, separated from the shore by a wide channel suitable for ships.

Coral reefs of far lesser extent are common throughout the Caribbean, particularly around the islands, for all lie within the tropic zone and no upwelling of cold water occurs to chill them. Florida also extends far enough south to be partly in the tropics, but the conditions along the Atlantic coast differ considerably from those of the Gulf coast of Florida. As the Gulf Stream sweeps to the northeast some miles off the Florida Atlantic shore, cool water is drawn up closer to shore to replace what is drawn away, and the sea temperature is too low for coral reefs to exist. Along the Gulf coast no such influx of cool water takes place; in the southern region, where the water is warmest and also farthest from the discharge of silt from the Mississippi River, coral reefs and the life they support are abundant.

A coral-reef park

One of the finest reef areas is the beautiful John Pennekamp Coral Reef State Park extending out from Key Largo and including nearly seventy-five miles of living coral. Here, with ease and safety, anyone can see a large reef at its best, replete with corals of many kinds, such as staghorn, moosehead, star, finger, flower, and cactus coral, all names descrip-

Sea whips (*left*), an inch in diameter and sometimes as tall as a man, are horny corals that grow in shrublike stands at the base of the reef. Thickets of brittle staghorn coral (*right*) may extend over acres, providing safe haven for fishes and other reef dwellers.

155

THE GREAT BARRIER REEF

Like a giant breakwater stretching for 1250 miles along the northeastern coast of Australia, the Great Barrier Reef is the largest system of coral formations on earth. At some points along its length, the reef is more than a hundred miles from the Australian mainland; elsewhere it veers to within ten miles of the coast. The outer, or eastern, side of the reef forms a mighty rampart all the way to the ocean floor, five hundred feet below. Against this wall the Pacific Ocean batters with awesome fury. The inner side of the reef shelters a vast lagoon where the average water depth is only 120 feet.

The Great Barrier Reef is actually not a single reef, but rather a complex system of individual reefs, islands, channels, and shoals. At low tide, great expanses of the reef are laid bare, offering the richest display of marine life in the world. Every tide pool holds a seemingly endless variety of sea creatures—dazzling reef fishes, vivid blue starfish, literally hundreds of different kinds of coral. Everywhere are the giant clams, some weighing a quarter of a ton, for which the reef is famous. The reef is not without its dangers, however. Its inhabitants include a pretty little cone-shell snail that can kill a man with a jab of its venomous tongue, and the notorious stonefish, the deadliest and ugliest fish in the sea. But despite these dangers, the Great Barrier Reef is nature's finest showcase of the wonders of life in the ocean.

AUSTRALIA

GREAT BARRIER REEF

CORAL SEA

Swift and sharp-eyed, this six-foot barracuda probably would not molest a human swimmer, unless it mistook a sudden movement or a flash of jewelry for a fish. If it should attack, its razor teeth could take off an arm or leg in a single strike. The smaller fish are skipjacks, enjoying the protection—and somehow avoiding the jaws—of this big predator.

tive of their shape. Reef fish, turtles, crabs, conches, barracudas, and sharks live and breed within this tropical coral community, not to mention the evil-looking moray eels. A web of life in magnificent color, variety, and complexity spreads out like a beautiful tapestry. How is it put together?

Because reef-building corals depend partly on the microscopic plant cells they contain, they are able to grow down to a depth of only a hundred feet or so. Below that the light intensity becomes too weak to support photosynthesis, and coral growth ceases. However, reef corals can survive the loss of their plant cells for a while, and occasionally they have to do so. Certain regions of the tropics, such as the Caribbean, are buffeted annually by hurricanes. Now and then a great deluge of rain from a hurricane falls over reef areas and dilutes the seawater bathing the corals. When this happens, the plant cells throughout the coral tissue are killed, and the corals then lose much of their distinctive color and take on a bleached appearance. If the dilution by fresh water is severe, many corals die—particularly those growing within a few feet of the sea surface. As a rule, however, the majority survive and before long become reequipped with a new supply of plant cells. This is not surprising, since apparently the same kinds of dinoflagellate cells live independently in the tropical sea and are ready to infect, so to speak, any coral polyps that may capture them.

Try descending carefully from the edge of the coral reef, equipped with flippers, goggles, and snorkel, if not the full scuba-diving equipment. Move carefully from the outermost edge that slopes steeply down into deep water. At the edge of the surf you will first see massive roundish and pillar-

A moray eel may be lurking in any hole or crevice in the coral reef, and so the prudent skin diver does not probe into such openings with his bare hands. Most of the world's eighty species of morays reach four or five feet at full growth, but ten-foot giants are occasionally seen. The moray generally keeps to its hiding place by day, emerging after dark to hunt. Its most frequent prey is the octopus; the deep lairs favored by the octopus provide little sanctuary against the attack of an eel, which can easily slither down because of its snakelike shape.

BUCK ISLAND REEF NATIONAL MONUMENT

If you are interested in ocean life and have a chance to visit the American Virgin Islands, don't miss Buck Island, just an hour's pleasant boat ride from the large island of St. Croix. Here you can see a good many sea creatures without even getting your feet wet: marine turtles come here to lay their eggs, and the island has fine colonies of frigatebirds, pelicans, and other ocean birds.

Commercial charter boats leave regularly for Buck Island from Christiansted, St. Croix. The boats have guides for the underwater nature trail, and even the most inexperienced swimmer is quite safe in their expert hands. As in all National Park Service establishments, visitors are not allowed to collect or otherwise molest the wildlife.

But Buck Island's chief attraction is its splendid coral reef, one of the finest in the Caribbean and now established as a national monument under our National Park Service. The reef features a unique underwater nature trail, along which you can see many of the fishes, corals, and other creatures described in this book. No skin-diving experience is required. Competent instructors will teach snorkel-and-flipper technique in just minutes; and if you can dogpaddle, you have all the swimming skill you need. The entire day's outing—round trip by charter boat, equipment rental, guides, and lunch on the island—costs less than ten dollars, and it may well be the highlight of your vacation.

Buck Island's reef is the true barrier type, rare in the Caribbean. The water on the island side of the reef is calm, crystal clear, and free of sharks and other potentially dangerous animals.

ANTLER CORAL FOREST

THE CORAL ANIMAL SECRETES LIME
AROUND ITS BODY FOR PROTECTION
IN TIME, MILLIONS ATTACHED TO A COMMON
BASE, FORM BEAUTIFUL CORAL FORESTS

A fine stand of antler coral (left) is one of the features of the underwater trail at Buck Island National Monument. The entire trail can be covered in about twenty minutes if you don't stop and look. Most visitors, however, spend about an hour, frequently pausing to watch the interesting inhabitants of the reef, such as the parrot fish shown above. Parrot fish have a well-developed sense of territory rights; this one mistakes its own reflection for an intruder. Protective glass covers make it easier to keep descriptive placards free of algae and other fouling organisms. Below, two snorkelers go down for a closer look at a pair of massive brain corals. The average water depth along the underwater trail is ten to twelve feet.

This many-armed feather star is a member of the Crinoidea, one of the most ancient of all groups of marine animals. Three hundred million years ago, crinoids filled the seas in astonishing abundance: 2100 species have been identified from fossilized remains.

shaped corals such as *Porites* and *Millepora*. These so-called stinging corals, whose shape enables them to withstand the pounding waves, constitute the cornerstones of the reef. Together with the reddish calcareous, or coralline, algae, they usually encrust or cover over dead coral, thereby converting the dead material into a harder substance. These are the real reef builders and, as such, they are necessary to the existence of the more spectacular corals.

The branching corals that give the deeper parts of a reef the appearance of a forest of stone are to be found at greater depths, where wave action is less likely to break their brittle branches. Greater numbers of loosely branching and fragile kinds are found with increasing depth and water stillness. At these depths, however, the water has already absorbed much of the light, particularly the red light. Whatever the actual colors of the corals and their inhabitants may be when brought to the surface or when photographed by flashlight, all appear to be drab, dull greens and browns in the greenish-blue water. To see the full color of the reef, you should walk in shallow water at the reef's edge when the tide is low. Better yet, sit down in water a couple of feet deep and look carefully through goggles at everything around.

Much of the life of the coral reef appears to be no more animated than the stony corals themselves. Red, yellow, and purple sea fans and sea rods find anchorage among the stony coral bases. Covered as they are with delicate polyps exposed to the surrounding water, they resemble flowering bushes. Worms that burrow into the coral itself or build tubes between or attached to the coral protrude red, yellow, purple, and even blue flowerlike heads. The worms' bodies are protected from hungry passing fish or crabs, for their tubes are well out of the way; the decorative heads shoot back into the tube in a split second when the shadow of a fish passes over them.

Here also are sea squirts of many kinds and colors. Some of them are solitary individuals several inches long and as black as they can be, for the dense blackness protects their tissues from the intense light of the tropical sun. Others grow in clustering colonies, individually smaller but more striking altogether, forming vivid orange or purple mantles around the upper parts of sea fans and sea rods or the tim-

Despite their simple appearance, these adult sea squirts are members of the great phylum Chordata, which includes all the higher animals, from fish to man himself. The resemblance is more obvious in the sea squirt's free-swimming larvae, which look like tiny tadpoles.

bers of old and forgotten wrecks. Brightly colored feather stars extend their featherlike arms into the water flowing past as they hold on to sea fans and shift around from time to time. Lower down, extensive mats of green sea anemones carpet the dead coral, particularly along the sides of crevices.

The coral-reef community

All these various kinds of animals feed upon the microscopic plankton of the water that flows among them, filtering or sifting the water in various ways. They are all consumers dependent on the bounty of the water, although the corals, because of their cooperating host of internal plant cells, must also be ranked with the primary producers of the sea. And on these in turn depend a host of more active creatures. Gaily colored slugs, flatworms, and bristle worms wander among the polyp-bearing corals and sponges, feeding freely on their tissues in spite of the stinging cells of corals and the sharp spicules of sponges. Large black sea urchins, with long poison-tipped spines, and large black brittle stars shelter in the shade of the coral ledges when the sky is bright, but they venture out on the sand between the coral masses at dawn and dusk and whenever the light is not strong.

The coral-reef fish, often with queer and fantastic shapes and patterns as well as vivid colors, dart here and there among the branches and crevices of the coral jungle and flaunt their colors for all to see. They act as if they know they are safe from fish such as the predatory gray and yellow snappers and the barracudas that prowl along the reef's edge.

The waters of the tropical open ocean that reach the coral community contain food in the form of plankton, to be sure, but they are not so rich as the waters of colder seas. Plant life is limited mainly to that in the coral tissue, to the coral-like plants of the deeper reef, and to a film or low growth of

A pair of flamingo-tongue snails (*left*) graze on soft coral, stripping living tissue off the leathery skeleton. The sponge (*upper right*) is one of the simplest of the multicelled animals, being little more than a community of individual cells with no unifying nervous system. The brilliantly colored *Glossodoris* (*lower right*) is a nudibranch—"naked-gill"—so named because of the feathery cluster of respiratory gills near its rear end. All these animals are common members of the reef community.

A *school of blue tangs
threads through the coral of
a reef in the Bahamas.*

THE REEF FISHES

Of all the attractions of the coral-reef
community, none is more likely to
delight the human visitor than the
fishes. Their beauty and variety are
unrivaled anywhere else in the
animal kingdom. In place of the
blue-above–white-below of the
pelagic species and the drab
camouflage of the bottom dwellers,
the reef fishes display a seemingly
endless array of brilliant, often
startling color patterns.

At first thought, it would seem as
though such vivid coloration must
invite sudden death in a world where
a hungry predator is never very far
away. But if this were the case, these
bright colors would have been
eliminated long ago by the ruthless
process of natural selection. Indeed,
we must assume that these bright
liveries somehow benefit the animals
that wear them. How? There is no
single, pat answer, but some of the
underlying principles can be pointed
out.

First, the reef itself provides a
dazzling multicolored background, so
that these fishes are much less
noticeable here than they would be
in other waters. The reef also
provides endless nooks and crannies
for them to hide in when danger
threatens, putting less of a premium
on being overlooked by a predator.
Sharply contrasting bars and blotches
of color may also break up a fish's
outline, hiding the fact that it *is* a
fish. Some reef species employ

warning coloration:
distinctive patterns that
turn away would-be
predators by advertising
the presence of distasteful
flesh, venomous spines, or
some other defensive
characteristic. Apart from
these essentially protective
functions, coloration can
play other roles in the
continuity of a species.
Among schooling fishes,
for example, color
patterning is a means of
keeping the school
together and coordinated
in its movements. In
many species, color
display is associated with
courtship and mating
behavior.

Finally, as you look at the
fishes shown on these
pages, remember that you
look with the eyes and
the brain of a human,
and not with those of a
shark or a barracuda or a
reef fish. What you see
does not necessarily
coincide with what they
see.

*Here are four represent-
ative reef fish: two-inch
fairy bass from Saudi
Arabia* (left), *a fifty-
pound grouper from the
Bahamas* (upper right),
*a foot-long Koran
angelfish from the Loyalty
Islands* (lower right), *and
a five-inch emperor
gramma recently
discovered in Honduras*
(far right).

The lionfish is among the most
beautiful and the most deadly of
the reef fishes. The bristling spines
are lined with grooves containing
glands that produce a substance
chemically related to cobra venom.
These spines are more than merely
defensive armament; the lionfish
will actually charge an animal
venturing too close, jabbing at it
with the spines. A puncture from
a single spine will cause a human
excruciating pain, and a skin diver
blundering into a school of
foot-long lionfish could die an
agonizing death. Three species are
shown here: a Pterois volitans
(above), and a Pterois radiata and
four Pterois antennata (right).

vegetation covering the dead coral in shallow water. Sea urchins browse on such a film; so do certain fish, particularly the handsome, large-scaled blue and pink parrot fish that keep the reefs literally scraped clean of almost all seaweed growth. Wherever they are present, you can see the scrape marks that their parrot-shaped jaws have made on the rocks below the tide. As a whole, however, there is little enough food to go around, and a coral community is outstanding more for the great variety of its members than for large numbers of any one kind.

The giant clam

The reefs of the Indian and Pacific Oceans have one remarkable animal not present in the Caribbean. This is the giant clam *Tridacna*, the largest and most beautiful clam in the world. It lives not only in the reef itself but in shallow lagoons behind the living reef. The fluted, scalloped shell grows to a width of three feet and a depth of two feet and weighs two to three hundred pounds, although the animal within weighs twenty pounds at the most. All the same, this is a great amount of clam to maintain itself within a single bivalve shell.

The thick, gorgeous mantle edges of the living animal, colored deep blue and green and mottled with black, close the wide opening between the two shells completely, except for a pair of tubular siphons. These allow a current of water to pass into and out of the spacious interior, filtering out any plankton that is present. But the secret of the unusual growth of the giant clam seems to be the same as it is for corals. The colorful tissue of the exposed mantle, which faces upward toward the light, is packed full with the same sort of microscopic plants.

Once settled on the sea floor, the clam never moves except to open or close its shell. Yet in its own way it is just as marvelously made and suited to a particular way of life as the equally molluskan squid and octopus. The clam's way of life requires neither brain nor eyes, and it has none, while the squid and the octopus have both of high order.

The folklore of the sea abounds with tales of the giant *Tridacna* clam clamping down on the arm or ankle of a careless diver and causing him to drown. Has it ever really happened? Nobody seems to know for sure.

The gorgeous colors of *Tridacna*'s mantle vary from individual to individual, with no two exactly the same. Part of this coloration is due to the presence of algae that live within the mantle tissue and apparently play an important role in the clam's metabolism.

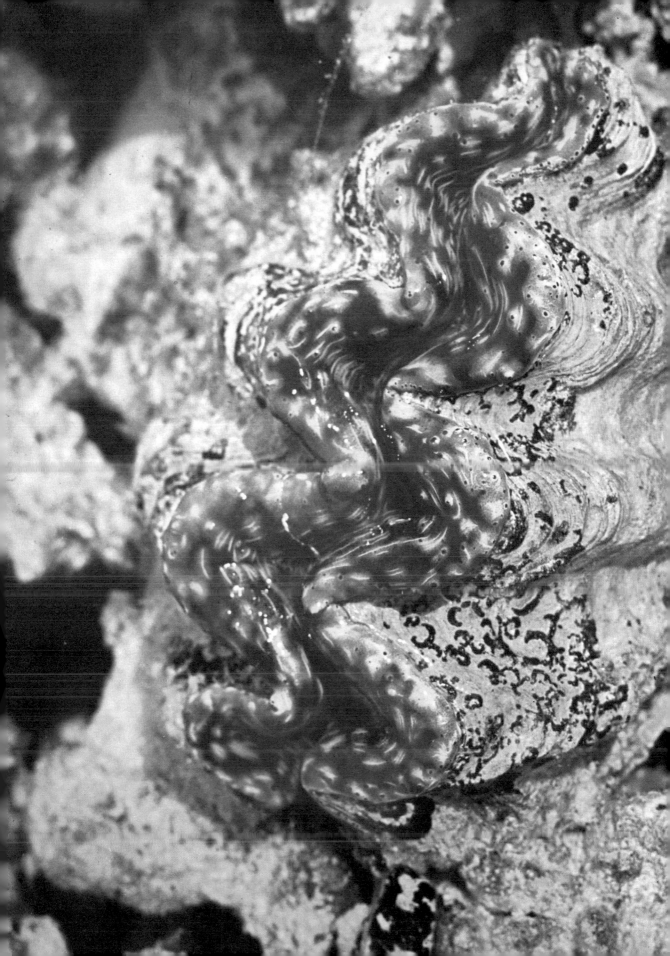

The octopus

Reefs the world over are also the home of the octopus. In spite of its reputation, an octopus is a timid, retiring creature with a liking for the same sort of crevices in reefs and rocks that appeal to the powerful, aggressive, and vicious mottled moray eel. Eels, in fact, are the bane of its existence, for a moray will go down into the hole of an octopus and make a meal of it.

Left alone, an octopus moves slowly about the reef by means of its eight sucker-equipped arms, searching for crabs and other crustaceans. Closely related to the squid, it has the same capacity for changing color to match its background. Unlike the squid, it has lost the molluskan shell and is able to squeeze its flexible body through the narrowest crevices in search of food. With a tentacle spread rarely more than four or five feet across, most octopuses remain small enough to take advantage of the narrow passages and crannies of coral reefs.

Life on the continental shelf

Kelp forests and coral reefs demand both light and a solid base. Only a small part of the shallow sea floor can satisfy these requirements. By far the greater part of the underwater platform extending to the edge of the continental shelf is too deep for either kelp or coral. Yet it is this deeper platform that supports the densest populations of marine animals anywhere in the ocean.

In the upper layer of the ocean where there is sufficient light, microscopic plants are the primary source of food for other forms of life, but all have to cope with the ever-present force of gravity. On the sea floor below, beyond the shallow fringe of the sea, the only living plants are the thin pink corallines that encrust dead shells and occasional stones. Animal life in this region must contend with the varying nature of the sea floor itself and must depend upon a different source of food. On the other hand, creatures that

The octopus concealed in the coral on the opposite page is shown more clearly in this drawing. The animal's most distinctive feature is the eight arms with their rows of suckers, one of which is shown enlarged. The sucker operates rather like an ordinary rubber suction cup: it is applied to the object to be held and its center is drawn upward by muscular contraction, creating a partial vacuum. The common octopus has 240 suckers on each arm, a total of 1920 per animal.

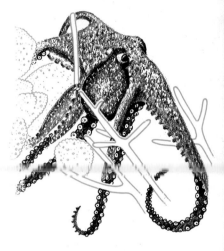

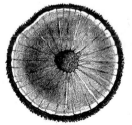

Despite its sinister reputation, the octopus is one of the shyest of the reef dwellers. If it cannot find an unoccupied crevice to live in, it will build itself a lair by scooping out a hollow in the sand and fortifying it with piled-up rocks and shells.

177

THE "DOCTORS"
OF THE CORAL COMMUNITY

A little four-inch wrasse (*Labroides dimidiatus*) has a particularly curious method of sustaining itself: it helps keep other fishes clean and healthy. Like patients in a doctor's waiting room, a school of goatfish and squirrelfish (*left*) wait their turns as one of these wrasses carefully goes over them, removing parasites and cleaning out sores that might otherwise become infected. The wrasse is a compulsive cleaner, and goes to work on anything that enters its cleaning station—including the toes of photographer Doug Faulkner (*upper right*). Even the most ferocious of the reef's inhabitants, such as the moray eel (*lower right*), willingly submit to the wrasse's treatment; and somehow they resist the temptation to eat it, even when it is working inside their mouths.

Similar cleaning duties are performed by several other fish, certain species of shrimp, and at least one kind of crab. When these cleaners are removed from an ocean area, the health of the local fish population rapidly declines.

These little blennies (left) *closely mimic both the coloration and the characteristic movements of the cleaning wrasses—but when a bigger fish approaches to be cleaned, the blenny bites out a chunk of flesh or fin and darts away. Adult fish usually are not fooled by these tactics, but youngsters have to learn the hard way to distinguish between friend and foe.*

THE
SHELF COMMUNITY

The continental shelf—a portion of the ocean floor embracing an area equal to the continent of Asia—harbors a rich and varied animal population. You have already met many of these animals in their larval stages, as temporary members of the plankton community; here you see them as adults, feeding on the steady, gentle drizzle of organic material from the surface waters above. Acorn barnacles have permanently cemented themselves to the rocks at the far left, and perpetually rake through the water for tiny food scraps with six pairs of feathery legs. Bottle-shaped sea squirts siphon water in one body opening and out another, capturing food particles in an interior lining of sticky mucus. The oysters, like the . . .

move or rest on the bottom need not contend with the force of gravity. They are free to grow large and heavy, and most of them do.

The primary food of the animals living on the sea floor below the level where plants can grow is the same kind that sustains the creatures of the twilight zone throughout the open ocean. It consists of small particles that are the dead or decomposed bodies of the plant and animal plankton sinking from overhead. This nutritious material, called *detritus*, descends to the sea floor like manna from heaven. It is particularly abundant on the continental shelf because generally the seas above are exceptionally well fertilized by the silt-laden rivers of the adjacent land, and the plant and animal plankton is correspondingly rich.

Bottom feeders

Depending on their manner of feeding, bottom-living animals that collect detritus are called suspension feeders, filter feeders, or deposit feeders. If we include the animals that prey on them, we can classify all the members of the community according to how much they move around, that is, as sitters, creepers, or swimmers.

Sifting water for whatever it may contain requires very little effort. In the upper layers of the ocean, however, the sifters usually have to work to keep from sinking, and at least to some extent they also have to move in relation to the surrounding water. But on the sea floor it is a waste of effort to sift particles from the water by moving around. The water over the continental shelf is always moving to some extent, and a fresh supply continually passes over any stationary object. Consequently the most effortless way for

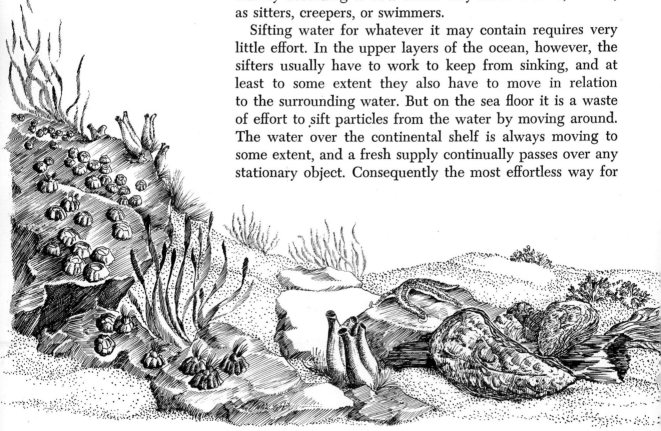

an animal to obtain a living is to sit still and draw the food-containing water over or through its sifting machinery. This is exactly what the sitters do, and there are many such creatures on the sea floor.

A sitter must anchor itself, so that it can make use of the water currents rather than be swept along by them, and then extend part of its body into the fairly clean water that is the source of its food. Where bottom currents are strong, generally bottom debris is carried away and bare rock ledges are exposed. On these live a variety of animals, particularly sea squirts, sponges, lamp shells, barnacles, and certain kinds of bivalves, all of them anchored permanently to the rock surface by some sort of cementing substance. Once they settle, as larvae, they are fixed for life, and the strongest current is unlikely to dislodge them. Throughout their lives they draw the passing water into their bodies and by one means or another sift out the microscopic organisms and organic particles.

Many filtering techniques

Sponges draw the water through tiny openings in their body surfaces and collect the microscopic particles that filter through their tissues. Bivalves and lamp shells draw water into the chamber between the two parts of the shell and pass it over extensive food-collecting surfaces called *gills*. Barnacles regularly protrude a handlike structure made up of six pairs of abdominal appendages that fan through the passing water like the strands of a cast net. Sea squirts draw the water through the siphonlike mouth into an oversized throat that is perforated like a sieve, so that food particles

. . . barnacles, have permanently attached to a firm substrate and feed by continually filtering water through their bodies, retaining whatever is usable. The leathery sea cucumber in the center of the picture gathers its food with the ring of sticky tentacles surrounding its mouth; one species, found in California, reaches eighteen inches. Behind the sea cucumber are two sea urchins, bristling with protective spines. The urchins are primarily browsers, working slowly over the bottom and eating whatever organic material they encounter. Next you see queen scallops, which, unlike most bivalves, are vigorous swimmers in their adult stage, always ready to jet out of the reach of their worst enemy, the starfish. In common with their relatives, however, the scallops are filter feeders. Finally, at the far right, you see a group of the curious little lamp shells, which at first glance look like bivalve mollusks, but are not, since the two shell halves are of unequal size and have a different sort of hinge. The lamp shells are the only members of a group called the brachiopods, characterized by a complex inner skeleton and a muscular stalk that passes through a hole in one of the shell halves. Like the bivalves they resemble, they are filter feeders.

pass on to the stomach and the sifted water passes out again through another siphon.

These water-manipulating creatures flourish wherever they can obtain a secure and permanent anchorage without being smothered by sand or mud. Rocks and pilings along the shore and ship bottoms everywhere are occupied by the same assortment of suspension-feeding sitters, with mussels and barnacles predominating in the colder seas and various oysters and sea squirts predominating in warm seas. But hard, firm surfaces, whether located inshore or offshore in deeper water, make up only a small portion of the submerged platform where food for sifters is abundant.

Starfish—enemies of oysters and scallops

Where rocky ledges do not protrude from the sea floor into overlying water, or where currents are not so strong as to sweep all debris away, beds or banks of rubble, coarse gravel, or broken shell offer the next best places for attachment. Here you can find common oysters, anchored by their lower shells, forming extensive beds. They are kept in place by the weight of their heavy shells as well as by the cement that holds them to whatever lies underneath. Scallops also live on the coarser stretches of gravel, though unlike oysters they move about freely.

Jet-propelled queen scallops take to the open water to escape a foraging party of their worst enemy, the starfish. In addition to a multitude of tiny eyes (visible here as dark dots along the fluted edge of each shell), scallops have well-developed senses of touch and smell that help them avoid these predators.

Beds of oysters and scallops attract starfish, especially the common starfish *Asterias,* which often move in hordes over the shallow sea floor in search of food. Even the thick shell and strong muscle of an oyster are no defense against starfish. Indeed, a flourishing bed of oysters can be entirely destroyed overnight by a starfish horde.

To devour an oyster, all a starfish needs to do is attach its numerous tube feet to the oyster's upper and lower valves. The pull is not strong, but it lasts longer than the oyster's muscle can keep its shell closed. Sooner or later the shell opens, and in goes the protruded stomach of the starfish.

Starfish invade scallop beds also, for scallops are just as nourishing and are more easily opened, if caught. Yet there is the rub, at least from the standpoint of a starfish: scallops, surprisingly, are able to swim and so generally escape. All around the scallop's mantle edge, along both the lower and the upper shell, is a fringe of tentacles and several hundred bright blue eyes—small eyes, to be sure, but effective nevertheless. The eyes are attuned to the slow movement of an approaching starfish and trigger a violent escape reaction. Once set off, the scallop rapidly opens and shuts its shell, gulping water and squirting it out through two openings on either side of its hinge. Whole schools of small scallops have been seen actively swimming in this way. Large scallops move with greater difficulty, but still fast enough to get away from starfish.

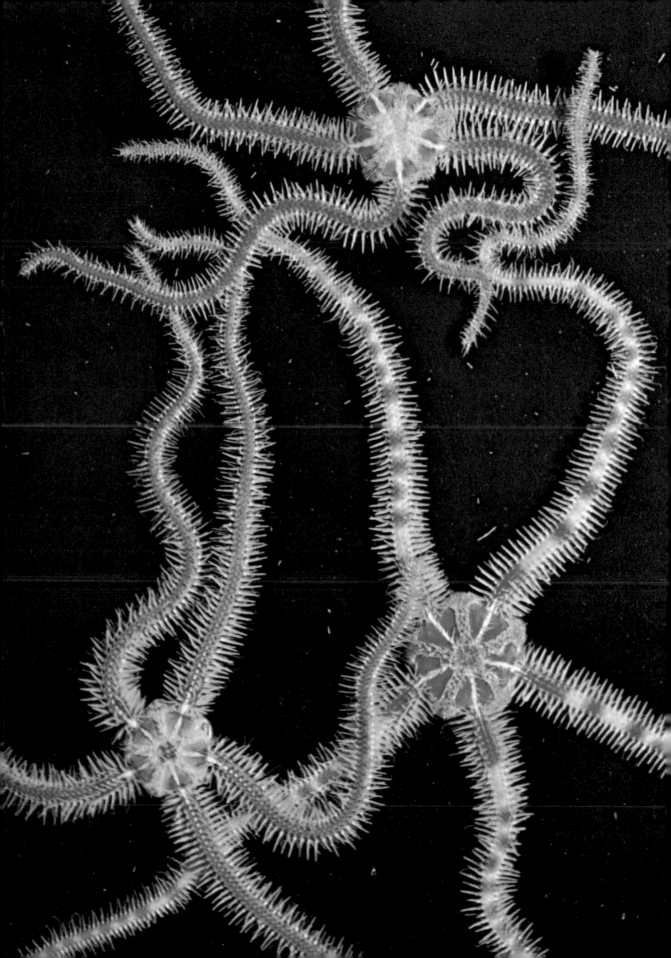

The undersea plains

A considerable portion of the vast plains of the continental shelf is neither base rock ledge nor the banks preferred by scallops and oysters. Where the current flow is relatively quiet and the rain of nutritive particles from above is steady, fine shell gravel, sand, and sandy mud are the general rule. In this material the bulk of the shelf life is to be found. Sea squirts usually are fastened at least to buried stones if not actually to exposed rock. They frequently form carpets of many acres, consisting of roundish individuals, about half the size of your fist, matted together shoulder to shoulder. When there is little to hold on to in the fine shell gravel or sandy mud, they fasten themselves together side by side, flush with the surface of the sea floor, with only their intake and output siphons protruding.

Elsewhere you may find brittle stars, those serpentine relatives of starfish, packed together so densely that their arms entangle. They form an extensive mat nourished by the detritus settling from above. Such brittle-star mats may extend for acres and exist for years.

Clams—creatures of the shallow sea

The most numerous filter feeders of the shallow sea floor are the clams of various kinds. Well adapted to living in the unstable substance at the bottom of the sea, they serve as food for many bottom-living fishes. The smaller kinds live embedded close to the surface, the larger ones somewhat deeper according to their size and shape. In all cases the two halves of the shell protect the animal from the pressure of the sand or mud in which it is buried, while two siphons extending to the surface draw in water for food and respiration. The deeper the clams bury themselves, the more secure they become. But the connection with the water above must never be lost, for all of their food comes from the intake of water.

The long neck clams have long siphons that reach to the

Brittle stars are also called serpent stars, because of the sinuous, snakelike movements of their long, flexible arms. Brittle stars possess remarkable powers of regeneration: even if all five arms are lost, the central disk may survive and grow new ones.

Clams occur in a variety of shapes and sizes, but all of them have generally similar living habits. The main body of the animal, including the bivalve shell, lies buried in the bottom sand or mud; a pair of siphons (sometimes housed in a muscular "neck") is the only communication to the open water. The role of the clams in the bottom community is similar to that of the crustaceans in pelagic waters: they convert semimicroscopic food-stuff into more substantial flesh that can be consumed by larger animals.

COQUINA

QUAHOG

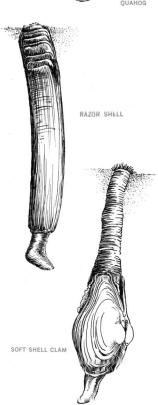

RAZOR SHELL

SOFT SHELL CLAM

surface but can be retracted if necessary. Even so, the necks of such clams are commonly found in the stomachs of bottom-feeding fish such as cod. The razor shells, with shells and bodies elongated like an old-fashioned razor, can move rapidly up and down a deep burrow as the need arises.

In their own way the sea-floor clams are as important to the community of the sea floor as the small crustaceans are to the community of the sunlit zone's green pastures. They accomplish much of the conversion of the continually falling nutritive particles into new living flesh and are the chief prey of the sea floor's predatory creatures.

A dangerous ability

In the course of time a clam or a sea squirt filters an astonishingly large quantity of water and extracts substances that can hardly be detected in seawater by laboratory analysis. For example, sea squirts and some sea cucumbers concentrate the element vanadium, which in sea squirts, at least, becomes an important component of the blood. It is the same element used in industry to make a certain high-grade steel known as vanadium steel. Clams of all sorts concentrate cobalt and strontium, heavy metals that are present in seawater only in traces. Clams and other creatures that absorb

Death of a coral-reef community: Bikini Atoll, 1946. Twenty years after this atomic test explosion, marine animals in the area still carry measurable traces of radioactive substances.

these elements from their surroundings do not distinguish between normal cobalt or strontium and the radioactive cobalt or strontium that has been produced through the explosion of nuclear bombs.

When hydrogen bombs were first tested over the western Pacific atolls among the Marshall Islands, radioactive material entered the sea as fallout. Clams and some other creatures concentrated it in their tissues, and so passed it on to others that fed upon them. Now, after many years, some marine creatures of this neighborhood are still unsafe for human consumption.

This experience should be a warning to us, for at present sealed containers of radioactive waste from atomic energy plants are being dumped into the sea. If any of these containers develop leaks and the waste escapes, the primary consumers on the continental shelf will undoubtedly concentrate it in their own tissues and pass it along the food chain to mankind.

The burrowers

Suspension or filter feeders are not the only sea-floor creatures to live on detritus. Much, if not most, of what falls from the upper water reaches the bottom without being taken by the sifters. The fine bottom deposits are therefore also rich sources of food, although the nutritive material becomes mixed with the sand ground from rocks and shells and the mud brought down by rivers. Deposit feeders must still sift in order to get food, but the sifting is of a very different kind. it is chemical rather than physical and takes place within the intestines of the animals. These are the creepers and particularly the burrowers, many of which are worm-shaped.

Worms, whether truly worms or not, burrow through sand or mud by literally eating their way forward. They pass the material in which they are burrowing through their bodies, for in no other way can the nutritive substances contained in it be digested out. Lugworms do this in mud, just as earthworms do in soil. Worm-shaped *Synapta*, close relatives of sea cucumbers and of starfish, do it in muddy sand. So do the equally worm-shaped "acorn worms," which have a remote relationship to fish and none at all to worms.

Other creatures do an equally effective job of burrowing. Elephant's-tusk, a small mollusk in a tooth-shaped shell with

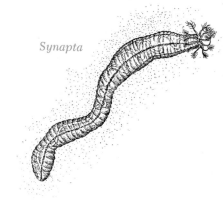

Synapta

The top layer of sand or mud on the ocean floor is a source of organic material exploited by the burrowers, two of which are shown here. Despite its wormlike appearance and habits, the six-inch *Synapta* is a relative of the sea urchin and starfish that has adapted to burrowing through mud. The two-inch elephant's-tusk is a marine snail that travels along just under the surface of sandy bottoms. Both these animals, in common with the familiar earthworm, literally eat their way through their surroundings, passing the mud or sand through their alimentary tracts and digesting out the organic material in the process.

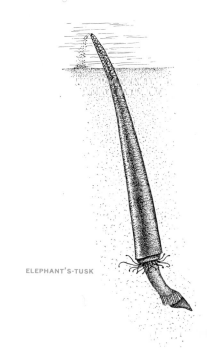

ELEPHANT'S-TUSK

If you dig up a heart urchin and set it on the bottom, it will bury itself again in about ten minutes. The heart urchin has lost the characteristic spherical shape of the sea urchin, in favor of a more streamlined egg shape that makes it easier to burrow along just below the ocean floor.

an opening at both ends, shovels sand in at one end and out at the other, moving along like an excavator. And in their own way sea biscuits, or heart urchins, work their way along beneath the surface of a sandy sea floor, passing the mixture of sand and nutritive matter through their intestines as they go. This is a remarkable accomplishment for spine-covered creatures closely related to sea urchins. Wherever food exists on or beneath the surface of the sea floor, some kind of animal is sure to find it.

Predators of the sea floor

These varied and abundant sea-floor creatures completely or almost completely buried beneath the surface are a rich source of food for animals of a more active kind. Many whelks and other sea snails browse on seaweed in the zones where it grows, but in deeper water they prey mainly upon the clams and worms. Small whelks feed on the smaller clams, large whelks on the larger clams; but all do so in much the same way. As a whelk or a moon snail plows along on the sea floor, its large muscular foot, and sometimes its whole body as well, is submerged beneath the sand and mud. The animal need only keep its respiratory water siphon protruded above the sediment so that clean water can always be drawn in. Whenever the snail meets a clam, no matter how tightly shut the clam's shell may be, it drills a neat round hole through the shell itself by means of a rasp on its mouth and makes a meal. Baby clams may even be devoured by burrowing worms, in particular *Nereis*, the clam worm, and its relatives, all of them armed with horny jaws.

At the sea-floor surface predators of many kinds are numerous. Brittle stars are everywhere; they not only form upward-facing networks of suspension feeders but also wander face down in search of clams, worms, or anything else that is not too large to eat. Starfish, including the many-rayed sun stars and the flat webbed starfish, roam everywhere, feeding on whatever they encounter, whether bivalves or crabs. Crabs, small and large, use their claws to break open sea urchins and thin-walled clams. Other crustaceans such as hermit crabs and shrimp are scavengers like the lobsters, although most kinds of lobsters will crush a clam or mussel if they find one. And so it goes: the sea floor is the scene of an almost free-for-all fight for food.

This enormous population of invertebrate animals, whether producers or predators, in turn supports vast numbers of fish. Many of the fisheries of the world are based on the bottom-feeding fish of the continental shelf. Cod, haddock, and others feed voraciously either on the assortment of invertebrates or on smaller fish that feed on these invertebrates, or on both. Flatfish such as flounder, sole, and halibut lie flat with one side down and both eyes on the upper side, the right or left as the case may be, watching for and pouncing on worms and other small creatures they happen to see. The skates and rays, wide-finned relatives of the shark but flattened from top to bottom rather than from side to side, glide here and there over the gravel and sand. As they pass closely over crustaceans, small fish, anemones, and small surface clams, they scent their prey and seize and crush them with flat nutcrackerlike plates of teeth.

Nereis, commonly called the clam worm, is one of the largest of the marine worms, sometimes reaching eighteen inches in length. It belongs to the same animal group as the familiar earthworm, but it differs from its dry-land relative in that it can deliver a vicious bite. Large numbers of *Nereis* worms burrow in sandy and muddy bottoms.

SKATE EGG CASE

The problem of growing up

This overall picture of the teeming flatland life of the continental shelf is incomplete unless we look at one of the major problems of existence in such a world: every kind of creature is born small and vulnerable and must grow up surrounded by enemies. Skates have overcome this disadvantage to a great extent by producing large eggs, about the size of bird eggs but enclosed in horny cases rather than brittle shells. From these eggs hatch relatively large fish that have little difficulty in surviving even at the start. The larger the eggs, however, the fewer that can be produced. The bony fish lay smaller eggs but many more. Most of them are eaten by other fish; of those fish that hatch, only a few succeed in living and growing through the long nursery period in the upper ocean to continue their hazardous existence down below.

Nearly all the bottom-living invertebrate animals produce enormous numbers of very small eggs which, in most cases, develop into minute larvae that spend considerable time feeding and growing as members of the plankton. Only a small percentage of these live to settle down on the sea floor, and those that do are still generally of microscopic size. This settling period is undoubtedly the greatest crisis in their lives: besides undergoing certain remarkable body changes at this time, they enter a world of dangerous proportions.

Size is relative. A grain of sand may be negligible to a full-grown clam or tube-living worm. To a microscopic larva about to settle down, it is enormous. Such a larva, of clam, worm, and many another, may actually settle on a single sand grain and have room to spare. For these larvae newly settling on the sea floor, the situation may be compared to that of a child who finds himself suddenly in a world of giant tumbled boulders many times his own size, among which he has to live and grow. And the settling takes place in territory already occupied by hordes of hungry creatures that browse on young and old alike. It is a wonder that any of the settling larvae manage to survive. Yet obviously they do, and one of the reasons is that they settle in tremendous numbers. Enough do survive to grow and maintain the sea-floor populations.

> All skates and some sharks produce eggs protected by tough cases of keratin, the substance of which hair, horns, nails, and feathers are made. At the right is the case of a skate egg, opened to show the developing embryo inside.

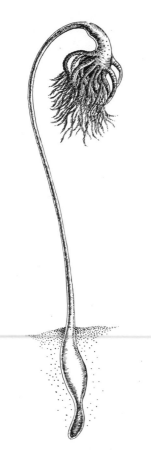

This sea pen, a relative of the corals, anemones, and jellyfish, lives in the deep ocean beyond the continental shelf, firmly anchored in the bottom sediment by a bulbous "holdfast." Intensely luminescent, sea pens light up in response to the slightest touch, the light spreading from the point of contact until the whole animal is aglow. The function of this luminescence is unknown.

A sea urchin rests on the ocean bottom more than a mile below the surface. Note the tracks and burrows of other animals. Man's knowledge of life at these depths is still sketchy, but new methods of deep-sea exploration are rapidly filling in details.

In the deepest water

Farther out to sea, closer to the edge of the continental shelf, the water deepens. The sea-floor lies farther from the surface, and below a certain depth the water becomes so still that the finest particles settle quietly on the bottom. The place where this begins to happen is called the *mud line*. And from the mud line near the edge of the shelf, all the way down the continental shelf and over most of the floor of the oceanic abyss, a soft watery ooze covers the solid floor. Whatever lives there must make its home on or in this ooze.

The water pressure at the lower depths is far greater than at the top of the continental slope, but it apparently has no effect on animals so long as no air or gas chambers are present in their bodies. The main problem of abyssal creatures, apart from the universal problem of obtaining food, is how to hold their place or to move about in the insubstantial ooze.

Abyssal creatures live at a depth of over a mile. Although their source of food is the steady rain of fine particles that descend from the upper sunlit ocean, much of the organic nutritive material has completely decayed or dissolved away before it reaches the deep-ocean floor. Consequently there is much less food to go round, and animal life, though present in wide variety, is thinly scattered compared with that of the continental shelf. What there is, however, consists of sitters, creepers, and burrowers as before, with an occasional fish to represent the swimmers.

The sitters, if we can still call them that, are usually elongated creatures rising from the ooze by one means or another. Beautifully structured glass sponges, with skeletons of glass spicules, stand like vases, supported in the ooze below by long glass strands that spread out like anchors. Sea pens, relatives of corals, stand like luminous many-blossomed flowers, supported by slender stalks with swollen bulbs at their lower ends well submerged in the ooze. Sea lilies, closely related to the active feather stars of coral reefs, have bodies and rays attached to the top of long calcareous jointed stems ending in spreading roots. Sea squirts, too, are

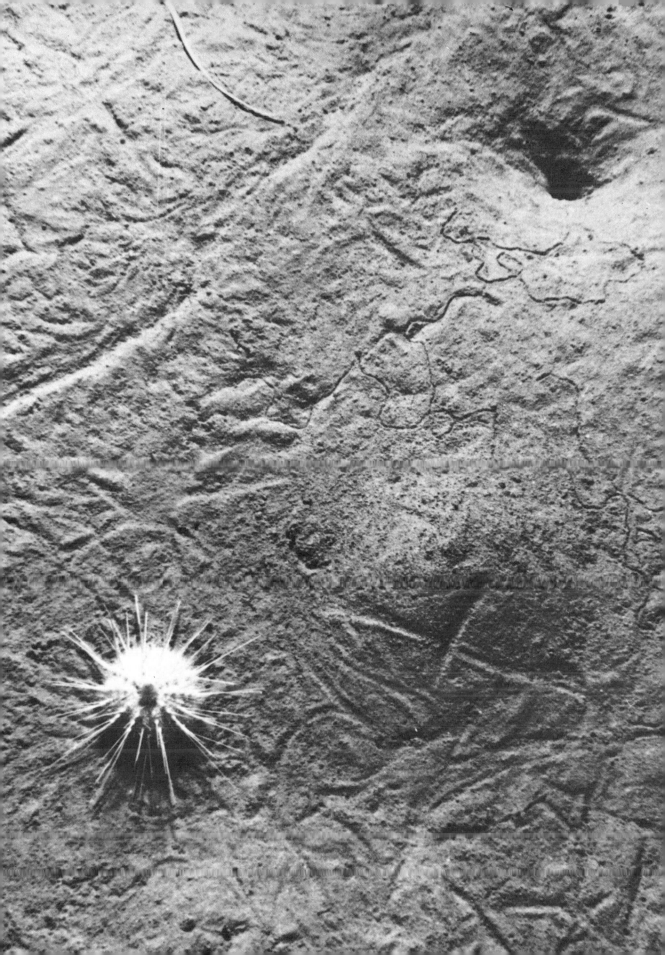

present, also with embedded stalks. All feed on any suspended matter that falls upon them.

Creatures such as these have been brought up in the deep-sea dredges of scientific oceanic expeditions, beginning with the great *Challenger* expedition of about a hundred years ago. What other life exists on the abyssal floor has only recently been discovered, and only partially at that. Now the bathyscaphe *Trieste* has descended to the floor of the greatest depths in the ocean, in the Mariana Trench of the southwestern Pacific Ocean. Photographs and the eyewitness reports of the observers on board show that many other kinds of animals are present, although thinly scattered. Crabs and shrimp walk across the surface of the ooze, their light bodies supported by relatively long and slender legs. Brittle stars with outspread arms and sea cucumbers, probably of no appreciable weight in the surrounding water, browse on the surface. Acorn worms and others burrow through the ooze. All these animals have been seen. But the variety and number of telltale tracks and other signs in the ooze surface clearly indicate that the vast majority of deep-sea creatures live in the ooze itself, out of sight.

The history of the world

The deep-sea ooze is interesting in itself. For the most part it consists of the dead minute skeletons of the plankton organisms that lived one to several miles above. The composition of the ooze in any particular area of the ocean floor depends on the nature of the commonest organisms in the plankton overhead.

Where diatoms predominate in the seas above, as in the Arctic and Antarctic Oceans, *diatomaceous ooze* made up mainly of glasslike diatom cases covers the sea floor down below. In more temperate regions the calcareous-shelled foraminiferan *Globigerina* far outnumbers everything else, and its empty shells accumulate below as *globigerina ooze*. The chalky White Cliffs of Dover and the cliffs of the

Bathyscaphe exploration has proved that the ocean supports life even in its deepest trenches, seven miles below the surface. This photograph was made from the United States Navy bathyscaphe *Trieste I*. The striped plate is used to measure the turbidity of the water.

THE OCEAN'S FLOOR

The floor of the world ocean is carpeted with a variety of sediments, which on the average are about a hundred feet thick. Geologists, physicists, biologists, and oceanographers all find the sediments a rich source of information to help them in their work.

In the waters near the land masses, the most common sediments are terrigenous, that is, derived from the land itself; they are carried into the sea by rivers and streams. Terrigenous deposits are fairly coarse—sand, gravel, gritty silt. In deeper water, vast expanses of the ocean floor are covered with red clay; this is also land-derived, but owing to its finer particle size it is carried farther out to sea before settling to the bottom.

Oozes are sediments derived from the remains of once-living ocean creatures. The most extensive of these is globigerina ooze, a calcareous sediment which covers fully one-half of the ocean's floor. Pteropod ooze, a calcareous deposit composed of the shells of pelagic snails, is found in certain areas of the Atlantic. Finally, the siliceous skeletons of diatoms and radiolarians produce two important sediments: diatom ooze in the cold latitudes and radiolarian ooze in warmer waters.

TERRIGENOUS DEPOSITS

RED CLAY

GLOBIGERINA OOZE

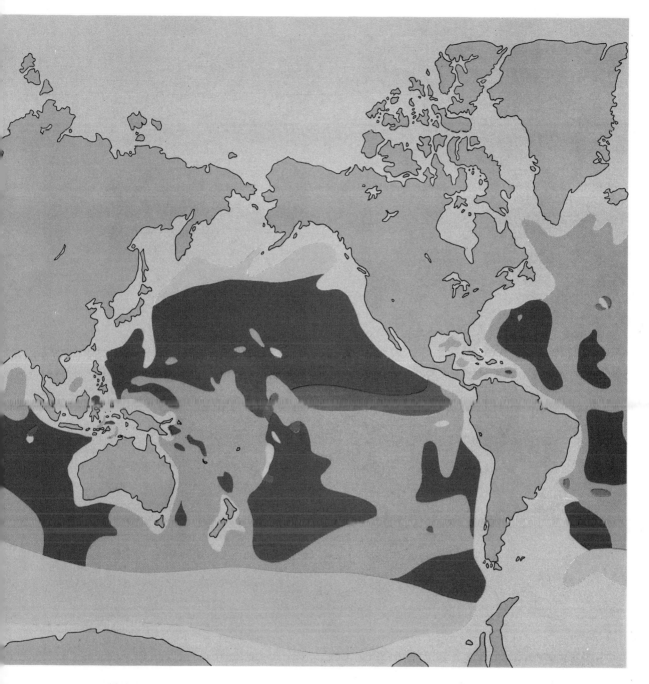

PTEROPOD OOZE

DIATOM OOZE

RADIOLARIAN OOZE

Normandy coast, on the opposite side of the English Channel, are made of globigerina ooze, consolidated as sea floor long ago and now drained of water and raised high above the level of the sea. Even the sea butterflies, the pteropods, are so abundant in certain areas of the tropical ocean that their shells form another kind of deep-sea deposit, called *pteropod ooze*. Beneath a certain depth, however, shells made of limy material dissolve during the long passage down through the water. Tropical seas, particularly in the Indian and Pacific Oceans, have great numbers of microscopic creatures, the Radiolaria, whose silicate skeletons do not dissolve. In these regions *radiolarian ooze* covers the deep-sea floor below.

As the years pass and more and more ooze accumulates, the deeper layers become increasingly solid. Gradually a dense base of firm material is formed. Such a base now overlies the real surface of the earth beneath the sea. The particular nature of the microscopic organisms at the ocean surface changes with the changing circumstances of current and temperature, and thus the nature of the skeletons in the ooze also changes. And so, as centuries and millennia roll by and layer after layer of consolidated ooze accumulates, the history of the earth is recorded in the changes. Deep-sea cores of bottom sediments are brought up from the depths by means of long ship-based cables and coring tubes. From studies of these cores the history of the ocean, and of the earth's climate as a whole, is slowly coming to light.

These massive chalk deposits, once at the bottom of the sea, were laid down a million centuries ago, through the slow accumulation of animal skeletons so tiny that you can hold millions of them in the palm of your hand. Time beyond measure, numbers beyond reckoning—herein lie a fascination and a challenge that forever draw man back to the ancestral ocean in an effort to understand not only the world he lives in, but himself as well

Appendix

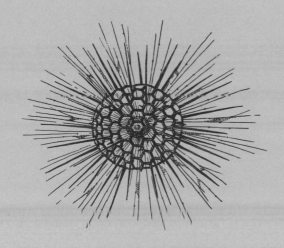

Ocean Life and Our National Park System.

On August 25, 1916, Congress established the National Park Service, a bureau of the Department of the Interior charged with the responsibility of administering a system of parks, monuments, and recreational areas "for the benefit and enjoyment of the people," and of conserving "the scenery and the natural and historic objects and the wildlife therein in such a manner as will leave them unimpaired for the enjoyment of future generations."

In its first half century of existence, the National Park Service has maintained a remarkable system of untouched tracts of natural wilderness. Each of these areas offers you the opportunity to see America as it looked before the first European settlers landed on the continent. Each affords you the chance to enjoy a variety of wildlife living under completely natural conditions.

A great many of the birds, mammals, fishes, and other creatures you have read about in this book can be seen in their natural habitats at the seashores and wildlife refuges included in the National Park System. And as the Park System continues to expand, more and more of the life of the ocean will be made available for the enjoyment and enrichment of us all. Since its establishment in 1961, for example, Buck Island Reef National Monument has introduced the splendors of the coral community to thousands of Americans who otherwise would never have seen them. A proposed similar underwater preserve in Florida, tentatively called the Biscayne Bay National Monument, will bring the strange and beautiful reef world even nearer.

A few of the many National Park Service areas where sea life can be observed are described here.

Acadia National Park (Maine)
Located on Mount Desert Island and Isle au Haut, just off the coast of Maine, Acadia has cold, fertile waters teeming with sea life. The sea plants are here in abundance, from microscopic diatoms to hundred-foot-long seaweeds. In a maze of tide pools, each a miniature ocean world, you can see starfish, anemones, barnacles, sea urchins, crabs, and marine snails in action. Acadia is a bird watcher's paradise, too—275 different species, including many ocean birds, have been recorded in the park.

Biscayne Bay National Monument (Florida)
This proposed national monument, which requires only a presidential proclamation to become a reality, would bring under National Park Service administration a large expanse of the warm, clear waters of the upper Florida Keys. The new national monument would either include the famous John Pennekamp

LOBSTER

Coral Reef State Park, now operated by the state of Florida, or else form a northward extension of it. In either case, tens of thousands of acres of unspoiled coral reefs and other marine habitats would be preserved and protected from commercial exploitation.

Buck Island Reef National Monument (Virgin Islands)

On December 29, 1961, President John F. Kennedy signed a proclamation establishing mile-long Buck Island and its superb barrier reef as a national monument under the control of the Virgin Islands National Park. Buck Island's underwater nature trail opens up the wonders of the coral reef to everybody. Because spearfishing and collecting are strictly prohibited, the animal population of the reef can be seen and appreciated under perfectly natural conditions. The island itself has been left wholly undisturbed, except for the addition of docking, picnicking, and toilet facilities, affording visitors the chance to wander on a true desert island just an hour from the city of Christiansted, St. Croix. (See pages 160 to 163.)

Cabrillo National Monument (California)

Cabrillo National Monument was established primarily to commemorate the discovery of the California coast by Juan Rodríguez Cabrillo in 1542, but it also holds two unusual attractions for nature lovers. One is the annual migration of the California gray whale, described on pages 82 and 83; the other is the strange spawning behavior of the fish called the grunion, described in *The Life of the Seashore* in this series.

Cape Cod National Seashore (Massachusetts)

Still under development, this national seashore will ultimately encompass 25,000 acres of natural beaches and dunes in an area that has long been a favorite haven of vacationers. Sea birds are abundant; the fishing is excellent; and there are reminders everywhere of New England's once-great whaling industry. Marked trails, lecture programs, and naturalist-guided tours are provided by the Park Service.

HORSESHOE CRAB

Cape Hatteras National Seashore (North Carolina)

Here is a chain of barrier islands extending for seventy miles along the Carolina coast, in places as much as thirty miles from the mainland. The wildlife is abundant and varied. Three hundred species of birds can be seen here, including several species that would be difficult to find anywhere else in the country. Porpoises are sometimes sighted just yards from the shore. For the fisherman, the surrounding waters offer channel bass, bluefish, marlin, tuna, and mackerel. The hunting of migratory waterfowl is permitted in designated areas of the park, subject to Park

203

Service rules and regulations. Camping sites, nature trails, special exhibits and programs, protected swimming areas, and boat-launching facilities all enhance this fine stretch of wild, wind-swept seashore.

Channel Islands National Monument (California)

This national monument includes Santa Barbara and Anacapa, two small but spectacular islands off the coast of Southern California. These seldom-visited rugged islands provide refuge for huge nesting colonies of sea birds and an exceptional variety of ocean mammals. California sea lions are in permanent residence, sunning themselves on the beaches and filling the air with their nearly continual barking. The huge elephant seal can be seen here, too, as well as the rarer Guadalupe fur seal. Even an occasional sea otter is sighted, and conservationists hope that this rarest of American marine mammals may someday return to these islands where it once thrived.

BABY PELICANS

Everglades National Park (Florida)

One tends to associate the Everglades more with swamp life than with ocean life, but marine animals are very much in evidence along the fringes of this huge national park at the very tip of the Florida peninsula. Here you can watch big brown pelicans fishing by plummeting into the sea from heights up to sixty feet. The big sea turtles come ashore at Cape Sable to lay their eggs. And with luck you may spot a manatee, the shy, ponderous ocean mammal whose relatives gave rise to the mermaid legends.

Fort Jefferson National Monument (Florida)

This national monument comprises the seven small coral islands called the Dry Tortugas, in the Gulf of Mexico just west of the tip of Florida. The islands are noted for their birds, and you will find frigatebirds, boobies, gulls, terns, and many others here. A popular pastime for visitors is wading in the surrounding waters with a glass-bottomed bucket or box to see the abundant fishes and invertebrates that populate the crystal-clear waters. But Fort Jefferson is only for the hardy: no housing, meals, transportation, or supplies are available.

Olympic National Park (Washington)

This famous mountain park includes a rugged fifty-mile-long strip of the Pacific coast, many parts of it accessible only on foot. The Olympic coast is one of the most unspoiled ocean fronts remaining in the United States. Sandy beaches, rocky cliffs, tide pools, and offshore islands frequented by seals and sea birds make this a supremely varied and scenic seashore.

Padre Island National Seashore (Texas)

Here are eighty miles of uninhabited seashore on a barrier island that marches along the Gulf coast just north of Mexico; it is the longest undeveloped beach remaining in the contiguous United States. Padre Island is noted for its pleasant climate, good beaches, abundance of shells, excellent surf fishing, and varied bird life. In addition to huge flocks of wintering waterfowl, the bird population includes herons, terns, egrets, brown pelicans, white pelicans, frigatebirds, and many others. But the island's finest qualities are solitude and the opportunity it affords for enjoyment of the ocean and its life in an area untouched by civilization.

Point Reyes National Seashore (California)

This beautiful peninsula north of San Francisco is bordered by broad beaches backed by tall palisadelike cliffs. There is a large resident herd of sea lions; ocean birds colonize the offshore rocks; sheltered lagoons harbor interesting animal communities; and windswept bluffs offer magnificent vistas of the Pacific Ocean.

Virgin Islands National Park (Virgin Islands)

This tropical island park covers about two-thirds of St. John, the smallest of the three major American Virgin Islands. St. Thomas, a neighboring island, is only four air hours from New York; the park is a thirty-minute boat ride from St. Thomas. The park features sandy beaches, sheltered coves, and extensive offshore coral reefs. Swimming, fishing, snorkeling, and underwater photography are all popular pastimes. Trunk Bay, on the north side of the island, offers a self-guiding underwater nature trail.

BLUE MARLIN

Endangered Ocean Animals

The bounties of the sea are not inexhaustible. Pictured here are four animals which, through human carelessness and greed, have been driven to the very brink of extinction. They are representative of a long list of creatures threatened with the same end.

Human activity is by no means always responsible for the passage of a species into oblivion. Nevertheless, man must bear the full blame for the total extermination of several hundred different animals, fishes, and birds during the past three centuries, and for so severely reducing the numbers of hundreds of others that replacement will be slow, painful, and, in some cases, impossible. No chapter in this bloody record has been more

GREEN TURTLE

This four-foot, five-hundred-pound turtle is found in warm, shallow waters all over the world but has virtually vanished from United States shores. One factor is the continued destruction of our natural seashore, where these creatures lay their eggs. Another is that both their flesh and their eggs are prized as gourmet foods. Most southern coastal states now have laws protecting the green turtle, and government research projects are under way to find new methods of rebuilding the population.

SEA OTTER

This big sea-going member of the weasel family grows to four and a half feet and weighs up to seventy-five pounds. Perhaps more than any other marine animal, the sea otter has been the victim of man's greed and cruelty. Once common all along the Pacific coast, hundreds of thousands of sea otters were slaughtered by nineteenth-century fur hunters who simply waded among the trusting animals and clubbed them to death. The result was apparent total extermination along our shore, but in 1938 a tiny colony of the animals was discovered off Monterey County, California. Under rigid state and Federal protection, this colony is slowly growing, with an estimated 1965 population of nine hundred individuals. A somewhat larger colony exists in the Aleutian Islands.

shameful than the slaughter man has committed in the oceans.

Happily, we may feel a little cautious optimism for the future. Meaningful national regulations and international treaties are beginning to impose long-needed restrictions on the whaling, sealing, and fishing industries. Marine biologists and oceanographers are teaching us how to enjoy the riches of the sea without depleting them. Perhaps most important of all, there is a growing public awareness that *all* wildlife constitutes a priceless legacy for future generations. But the task is great, and the necessary work is scarcely begun.

The four animals shown here, then, symbolize both the damage man has caused in the ocean and the steps he must now take to reverse it. It is essential that these steps be taken today. Tomorrow will be too late.

CALIFORNIA GRAY WHALE

The California gray is typical of the many species of whales brought close to extinction by unlimited commercial hunting. Now fully protected by international treaty, this animal is making a good recovery. An aerial census made in 1961 revealed an estimated population of six thousand individuals; by 1965, the count was up to eight thousand. Migrating northward to their summer headquarters in the Arctic Ocean and the Bering Sea, or southward to their calving grounds off Baja California, Mexico, small groups of these whales are commonly sighted in the inshore waters of the Southern California coast. A baleen whale living on small ocean organisms, the California gray reaches a length of nearly fifty feet and may weigh upwards of thirty-five tons. Its slate color, often mottled with barnacles, gives it its common name.

ATLANTIC RIGHT WHALE

The Atlantic right whale is another of the baleen whales that has been nearly exterminated by commercial hunting. It reaches upwards of sixty feet in length, one-quarter of which is taken up by the huge head. The overall black coloration, arching mouth, and horny "bonnet" on the head distinguish it from its relatives. The Atlantic right is one of the slower of the big whales, and so was relatively easy prey even before the advent of powered whaling boats and explosive harpoons. By international agreement, no Atlantic right whales are now being hunted; whether this step was taken in time remains to be seen.

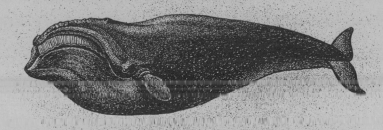

Sharks and Their Relatives

No group of ocean creatures attracts as much human fear, hatred, and interest as the sharks and their relatives, the skates and rays. No group of higher animals is less understood—or more misunderstood. Which species are dangerous to man and which are harmless? How are shark attacks provoked and how can they be prevented? Why are attacks on humans now occurring in waters that had once been considered safe? Scientists are hard at work on these and other questions.

The sharks are a very ancient group of animals. Superbly adapted to their environment, they have changed little in millions of years. The shark differs from other fishes in several important respects. Its skeleton is formed of cartilage, or gristle, rather than bone. Since the shark has no air bladder, it must constantly swim in order to stay afloat; if it becomes motionless, it sinks like a stone. It lacks true scales. Its teeth grow in rows, in such a way that as one set wears out, a fresh set replaces it—a characteristic that we humans well might envy.

In general, the sharks have evolved two basic body plans: the beautifully streamlined shape of the pelagic species, and the flattened pancake form of the bottom dwellers.

Hundreds of shark species have been identified, and new ones turn up every year or two. A few typical ones are shown here.

BLUE SHARK (15 to 20 feet long). This is the shark most commonly sighted in the open ocean. It can probably be classed as not dangerous to man; it feeds on small fish, squid, and carrion. Blue sharks will follow ships for days, feeding on the garbage tossed overboard. A prolific species, the female gives birth to as many as fifty live foot-long pups.

WHITE SHARK (normally 8 to 12 feet long, but recorded up to 36½ feet). This shark, also called the man-eater, is responsible for most of the authenticated shark attacks on human beings. An incredibly voracious animal, the white shark tends to devour its prey whole.

THRESHER SHARK (15 to 20 feet long). The thresher feeds on schooling fish—mackerel, bluefish, menhaden, herring, and the like. It uses its specialized tail to drive its prey into a compact, easily attacked group. Sometimes several threshers will team up in this herding activity and then move in for a shared feast.

HAMMERHEAD SHARK (8 to 15 feet long). Hammerheads are definitely among the species dangerous to man and, unfortunately, are among the most plentiful. The function of the oddly shaped head is not fully understood, but the projecting lobes may be used as steering planes to increase the animal's agility and maneuverability. The hammerhead's diet includes sting rays, bottom-dwelling fishes, and other sharks—including other hammerheads.

BASKING SHARK (30 to 45 feet long). In spite of its size, this is a harmless species, a plankton feeder that swims slowly along the surface and strains its food from the water with gill rakers. When the shark feeds in this manner, its back is well above the surface of the water. Several individuals may feed together, all lined up in single file—explaining the basis of a great many "sea serpent" reports!

WHALE SHARK (30 to 50 feet long). This is the largest fish known to man. Full-grown individuals may weigh fifteen tons. A plankton feeder like its slightly smaller relative the basking shark, the whale shark is entirely harmless to man—except as an occasional menace to navigation. Boats and ships have been badly damaged after colliding with one of these massive, indolent sharks lazing on the water's surface.

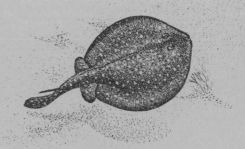

SAWFISH (16 to 20 feet long). Not as torpedo-shaped as the pelagic species, not as flattened as the bottom dwellers, the sawfish represents an intermediate step between the two typical shark body plans. Primarily a bottom animal, it uses its "saw" to slash through schools of small fish, stunning or killing individuals and then eating them at leisure.

ROUND STING RAY (16 to 24 inches long). The round sting ray is typical of the many ray species found in American coastal waters. It prefers a sandy, shallow bottom, where it feeds on mollusks, crustaceans, and other invertebrates. Its protective coloration, coupled with its habit of lying partially buried in the sand, make it difficult to see. Woe betide the wader who steps on one, for at the base of the tail is a barbed, venomous "stinger" that can inflict an extremely painful (but rarely fatal) wound.

DEVILFISH (4 to 5 feet long). We get only this relatively small species in our waters, but it is a near relation of the spectacular manta ray, which reaches 23 feet and 3500 pounds. The devilfish has abandoned the bottom-dwelling habit typical of the rays, and travels in schools near the surface, in quest of small fish and the larger forms of plankton. It sometimes leaps entirely out of the water, landing on the surface with a resounding smack.

COMMON SKATE (12 to 20 inches long). This is an abundant animal along our Atlantic shore as far south as Cape Hatteras, and is often found washed up on the beach after a storm. Although primarily a bottom feeder, it can also sally upward to capture and devour small fish.

210

Mammals of the Ocean

Life on earth originated in the ocean, slowly spread into fresh waters, and finally emerged onto dry land. In the course of eons of continuing evolution, some land animals have gradually returned to aquatic habitats. The biologist calls such animals *reentrants*. All ocean-dwelling mammals are reentrants; however fishlike some of them seem, they are all descended from ancestors who walked upon the land.

Three orders of the class Mammalia contain members that live in the sea. The carnivores (which also include the cats, the bears, the dogs, and a multitude of other terrestrial forms) are represented in the ocean by the seals, the sea lions, and the sea otters. The other two orders are entirely marine: the sirenians (the manatee and the dugong), and the cetaceans (the whales, dolphins, and porpoises).

These groups vary considerably in the extent to which they have become readapted to life in the ocean. The carnivores spend much of their time ashore, entering the water mainly to feed. The sirenians never leave the water but do stay close to land, passing their quiet lives in bays, lagoons, and river mouths. The cetaceans, finally, are fully committed to a pelagic life, and quickly perish if chance or misfortune causes them to leave the water.

Despite these differences in adaptation, all these animals share a group of characteristics that sets mammals apart from other vertebrates: they are warm-blooded; they breathe air; they possess hair; and they nourish their young with milk.

CALIFORNIA SEA LION (males 8 feet long, 600 pounds; females 6 feet long, 200 pounds). This intelligent, playful animal is the "seal" of the circus, although only females are so used, and must be captured young to be tamed and trained. A near relative is the much larger northern sea lion, the male of which weighs up to two thousand pounds.

211

ELEPHANT SEAL (males 20 feet long, 8000 pounds; females 11 feet long, 2000 pounds). The immense bulk of this animal (the largest living carnivore) and the huge inflatable snout of the male make its common name particularly appropriate. Elephant seals gather on sandy Southern California beaches during the day to doze and bask in the sun, and they enter the water at night to feed on fish, squid, and small sharks.

WALRUS (males 12 feet long, 2700 pounds; females 9 feet long, 1800 pounds). The walrus uses its long, distinctive ivory tusks for grubbing up the ocean bottom in search of the clams and other mollusks which (together with an occasional seal) form its diet. A heavy insulating coat of blubber protects the walrus from the icy Arctic waters where it makes its home.

HARBOR SEAL (5 feet long, 250 pounds). Our most common true seal, this attractive little creature, with its droll, doglike face, is found all along the Pacific coast and as far south as the Carolinas on the Atlantic coast. Harbor seals are often found far up into the fresh water in rivers and lakes. The pups make intelligent, affectionate pets.

MANATEE (12 feet long, 1200 pounds). Also called the sea cow, this sluggish, harmless creature spends its life browsing on aquatic vegetation in the warm, shallow coastal waters of Florida. The manatee has but one living relative, the nearly extinct dugong of the Indian Ocean. Despite protective laws, the manatee has also been brought close to extermination by thoughtless fishermen who shoot it merely to have something to use for a target.

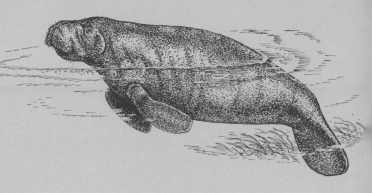

BLUE WHALE (100 feet long, 150 tons). Here is the largest animal that ever inhabited the earth, past or present. It seems strange that the blue whale, equal in weight to thirty-five elephants and dwarfing even the mightiest dinosaurs, feeds almost exclusively on inch-long crustaceans. The young are twenty-five feet long at birth.

SPERM WHALE (males 60 feet long, 50 tons; females much smaller). Although an air breather like all mammals, the sperm whale can remain submerged for well over an hour and dive to depths of half a mile in its search for the squid and octopus on which it feeds. Herman Melville's Moby Dick was an albino sperm whale.

KILLER WHALE (males 30 feet long; females 15 feet long). This big, intelligent, voracious predator has more than earned its other common name, the "sea wolf." Hunting in packs of up to several dozen members, killers prey on virtually every animal large enough to attract their interest: whales (even the larger ones), seals, sharks, penguins, sea birds, fish, and, when the opportunity presents itself, humans.

BOTTLE-NOSED DOLPHIN (8 to 12 feet long). Among the speediest of animals, bottle-nosed dolphins have been clocked at better than forty miles an hour. Dolphins apparently enjoy, or at least tolerate, the company of human beings. The folklore of the sea abounds with tales of dolphins helping drowning sailors to reach shore and saving swimmers from attacking sharks. The dolphin's remarkable intelligence, possibly comparable to that of the chimpanzee, has made it the object of much scientific study in recent years.

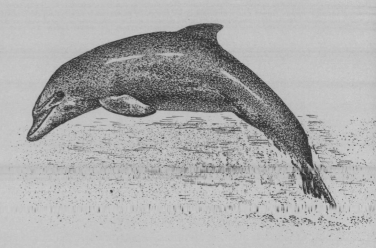

Man in the Ocean

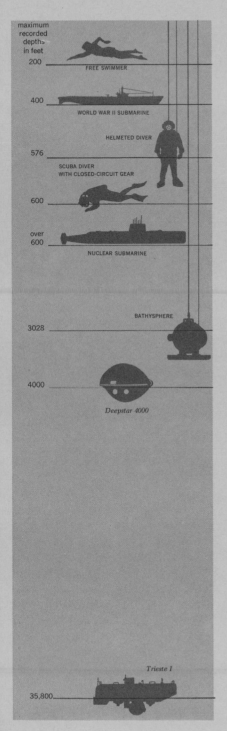

maximum
recorded
depth
in feet
200

FREE SWIMMER

400

WORLD WAR II SUBMARINE

HELMETED DIVER

576

SCUBA DIVER
WITH CLOSED-CIRCUIT GEAR

600

over
600

NUCLEAR SUBMARINE

BATHYSPHERE

3028

4000

Deepstar 4000

Trieste I

35,800

On January 23, 1960, two men climbed aboard an ungainly-looking craft that was bobbing like a cork in the choppy waters off Guam Island. Sealing themselves in a six-foot instrument-studded steel ball hanging from the craft's underside, the men operated the controls, and the craft began to sink into the Pacific Ocean.

The craft was the bathyscaphe *Trieste I*; its crew, oceanographer Jacques Picard and United States Navy Lieutenant Don Walsh; their mission, to make real a dream as old as civilization —man's longing to travel to the very bottom of the sea.

The *Trieste* sank steadily and silently through the calm waters far below the wind-whipped surface. Picard and Walsh were kept busy monitoring instruments, making readings, adjusting controls. After nearly five hours of steady descent, the *Trieste*'s trailing ballast chain touched bottom, and the craft slowed and came to a halt, hovering a few feet above the ocean floor. The dream had come true: two human beings, with 35,800 feet of water above their heads, were at the bottom of the Challenger Deep, the deepest known point in all the world's oceans.

For centuries, men had been striving to go deeper and deeper into the sea—in primitive diving bells, in submarines, in diving suits and bathyspheres dangling on long cables from the surface. The *Trieste*'s achievement culminated that effort and in effect closed the record books—there are no deeper dives to be made. But in a broader sense, the *Trieste*'s dive marked the beginning of a new era: the exploration of what has been called earth's inner space.

Three-quarters of our planet's surface is covered with ocean, yet less than five percent of that ocean has been explored. We know more about the face of the moon, a quarter of a million miles away, than we do about the sea floor that lies, at most, only seven miles below our feet. But our knowledge of the underwater world is expanding rapidly, and the conquest of the sea promises to be as exciting and as fruitful as the conquest of space.

The potential human uses of the sea are almost beyond imagination. As a source of food to support a burgeoning population, the ocean offers almost unlimited possibilities. Eighty-five percent of all earth life is found there, and much of it can be used, directly or indirectly, to feed human beings. "Aquaculture"— underwater agriculture—is still an infant technology, but it is already demonstrating the feasibility of the controlled cultivation of ocean plants and animals.

The staggering mineral wealth of the sea is only just now being tapped. Magnesium, a metal of major industrial importance, is "mined" from seawater. Vast beds of valuable metal ores cover much of the open-ocean floor. Gold, platinum, copper, and a host of other elements are present in seawater, waiting for the development of the equipment to extract them. We are rapidly depleting our reserves of dry-land mineral fuels—coal, petroleum, and gas—and here again the ocean offers rich sources of replenishment. Another increasingly scarce resource, fresh water, can be extracted from the sea; and in some parts of the world, water so obtained is turning age-old deserts into green farmland.

Of greatest immediate interest to humans is the portion of the ocean floor called the continental shelf, the relatively shallow area that skirts all land masses, and where the bottom lies no deeper than about 500 feet below the surface. At a 1958 Geneva conference, the United States and other countries were given title to the continental shelf along their coastlines. For the United States, this represents an acquisition of 800,000 square miles of new land—the largest addition to the nation since the 1803 Louisiana Purchase. Now we must devise the means of utilizing this vast new frontier.

One of the most pressing needs is for more versatile vehicles for undersea exploration. The *Trieste I* was basically a deep-sea elevator, a sort of underwater balloon not capable of much horizontal movement or of sustained periods of exploration. (Picard and Walsh were able to stay on the bottom of the Challenger Deep less than half an hour.) Scientists want far-ranging vessels

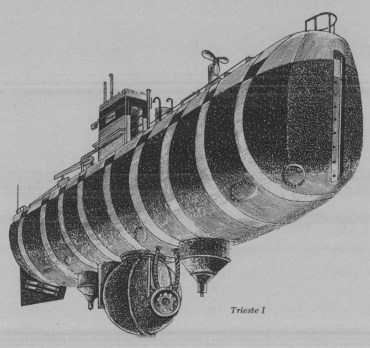

Trieste I

that can take human crews to depths of several thousand feet and maintain them there for days or even weeks.

The *Deepstar 4000*, developed by Westinghouse, is an example of such a device. It is a fully maneuverable vehicle that can take a crew of three to depths of 4000 feet and can pick up bottom samples, set out scientific instruments, and carry out salvage operations. A wide variety of other vessels are being designed and built, some by private industry, others under government sponsorship.

Finally, if a man is to exploit fully the riches of the ocean, he himself must learn to live there—to eat, sleep, and work there for considerable periods of time. A number of research programs are under way to find out how this can be done. A Navy project called Sealab II kept a crew of "aquanauts" working and living at a depth of 205 feet for 45 days. Conshelf III, a French project headed by pioneer diver Jacques-Yves Cousteau, operated at a depth of well over 300 feet for three weeks.

All these ventures are hesitant first steps into an era that promises to be the most rewarding since Columbus set sail to the New World. For thousands of years, man has been both attracted to the sea and frustrated by its basic inaccessibility. Within a single generation, the sudden shattering of this barrier of inaccessibility has opened up vast new continents filled with unimagined wealth, beauty, and adventure. Marine biology and oceanography have come into their own. For the men who study the sea and its life, the years ahead will be busy and fruitful ones.

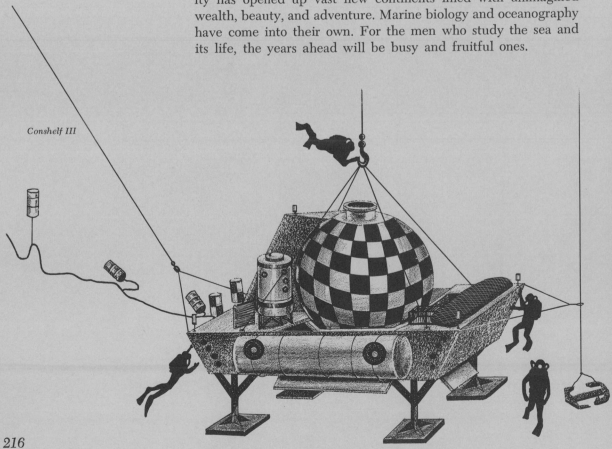

Conshelf III

Keeping Ocean Animals in the Home

A wide variety of marine animals can successfully be kept in a home aquarium, affording you a matchless opportunity to study these fascinating creatures at close range. You can enjoy this interesting hobby even if you live far from the shore; chemicals are available with which you can produce artificial seawater, and there are collector-dealers on both coasts who will air-express live marine specimens to your doorstep.

Apart from its esthetic and educational value, your home aquarium opens up the possibility of your making a genuine contribution to the science of marine biology. A vast amount of work is yet to be done in working out the detailed life histories of countless marine organisms. Don't be deterred by the lack of laboratory facilities, because in many such studies the most important tools are patience and careful, systematic observation.

A TEMPORARY AQUARIUM

Getting started

Marine animals are more demanding in their requirements than fresh-water species, but most of the rules for keeping a tank of ordinary tropical fish apply to a marine aquarium as well. It is wise to start on a small scale, adding to your collection as your experience grows. The equipment you need to get started is inexpensive and can be purchased at any pet store.

The aquarium itself may be anything from a wide-mouthed gallon jar (restaurants throw away numbers of these) to a commercial tank ranging up to thirty gallons or more. Smaller containers—up to about three gallons—are fine for temporary display of the simpler marine animals. For a more permanent setup, a bigger tank is both more satisfying and easier to maintain. A commercial ten-gallon aquarium would be a good starting point for the beginner. The all-glass or all-plastic type is worth considering, because most metals react with seawater to form substances poisonous to ocean animals. Since the same is true of soap, even in small traces, do not use it in cleaning an aquarium, and make sure there is none on your hands or arms. (Ordinary table salt, moistened with a little water and applied with a *new* kitchen sponge, makes a good scouring powder.)

Water for your aquarium can come from two sources. If you live near the shore, simply bring home as much as you need from the ocean itself. Use clean glass or earthenware containers. If your containers have metal tops, cover each container mouth with kitchen plastic wrap before putting on the top, to keep the water from coming in contact with the metal. It is a good idea to bring home an extra stand-by supply of water, in case of an aquarium emergency that necessitates a quick change of water.

If you live inland, you can make your own seawater with special chemicals available for this purpose. Do not try to use the so-called "sea salts" that were once popular for bathtub use; the kind you need is sold by pet stores. Follow the package directions carefully.

An inch or two of sand on the bottom of the aquarium will add to its attractiveness and will make its inhabitants feel more at home. Buy the kind sold for aquarium use. Beach sand tends to be too fine and is difficult to rid of various impurities. Unfortunately, marine plants do not do at all well in an aquarium and are best avoided altogether. Thoroughly cleaned shells and corals are acceptable and can be arranged in attractive displays that also offer hiding places for the more timid animals.

A simple device called a subsand filter will greatly simplify the task of keeping your aquarium clean. This is a perforated plastic plate that is placed on the bottom of the aquarium before the sand is added. A plastic tube attached to the plate receives air from a small air pump in such a way that the aquarium water is constantly drawn down through the sand and then discharged again through the tube. The sand itself thus acts as a filtering medium that breaks down waste matter and keeps the water sparkling clean. Very inexpensive diaphragm-type air pumps are available and are adequate for tanks of twenty gallons or less. The same pump should be used to aerate the water by bubbling air through an air stone. Aeration keeps the water well supplied with oxygen and helps carry off waste gases.

Finally, you should keep your aquarium covered to exclude dust and dirt and to cut down on evaporation. (House cats, too, are expert fishermen.) A sheet of ordinary window glass does the job. Take off the sharp edges and corners with a Carborundum stone or a piece of emery paper.

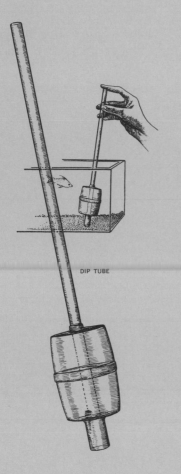

DIP TUBE

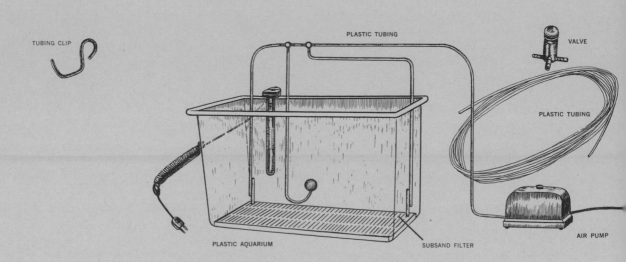

TUBING CLIP

PLASTIC TUBING

VALVE

PLASTIC TUBING

PLASTIC AQUARIUM

SUBSAND FILTER

AIR PUMP

Stocking the aquarium

Give the newly set-up aquarium a day or two to settle down, and then add the animals. Some may be purchased from local or mail-order dealers. If you plan to collect animals along the shore, remember that collecting is prohibited in *all* national parks and seashores and that other areas may be affected by state and local regulations.

Small half-grown specimens generally adapt more readily to aquarium life than do full-sized ones. *And do not overcrowd your tank:* ocean animals need much more living space than their fresh-water relatives. It is better to have a few healthy specimens rather than a tankful of sick and dying ones.

What animals are suitable? Among the fishes, you can try any of the small species (two inches or less) found in tidal pools. Many tropical-fish dealers stock clown fish (*Amphiprion*), a hardy, vividly colored little creature that lives among the stinging tentacles of the sea anemone. Dealers are also beginning to stock a wider variety of other exquisite coral-reef fish; but since these tend to be both expensive and delicate, the beginner will do well to pass them by for the time being.

A favorite of nearly everybody is the sea horse. The dwarf kind, which is widely sold through mail order, makes a particularly good addition to any marine collection.

From among the ocean's invertebrates you may choose anemones, sea urchins, small starfish, small shrimp and crabs, shellfish, live coral, sea slugs, and many others. Hermit crabs are particularly amusing to watch. With luck, you may obtain a very small octopus, perhaps the most fascinating of all.

Not all these animals will live together in harmony, and finding out which ones will may require some experimentation on your part. A good approach is to add one new specimen at a time and keep a close watch on the results for a day or so. If a clash develops, the offending party can be moved to other quarters.

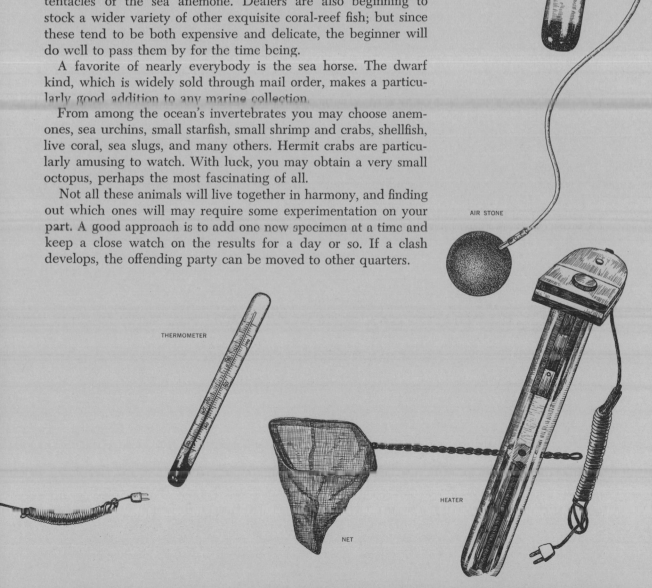

HYDROMETER

AIR STONE

THERMOMETER

NET

HEATER

Foods and feeding

Most marine aquarium animals thrive on a diet of readily obtainable foods. Fresh raw shrimp, fish, beef heart, lean beef, and crab meat are all suitable. Chop the food into pieces that your animals can accommodate; rinse it before feeding, to remove excess juices. Ordinary earthworms make a fine food and can be treated the same way. Canned minced clams are available at most grocery stores. With any of these foods, it is convenient to prepare a fair amount at one time and then freeze it in one-meal units wrapped in plastic wrap.

Many pet dealers stock *Tubifex* worms and frozen adult brine shrimp, both favorite foods of most marine fishes. If your collection includes any of the larger marine fishes, you can feed them live minnows that you catch yourself or buy at a fishing-bait stand. Sea horses insist upon live food. The easiest way to furnish it is in the form of newly hatched brine shrimp. Any tropical-fish dealer can supply you with the shrimp eggs and tell you how to hatch them.

Some marine organisms need vegetable matter in their diet. The best form of this is marine algae, although cooked spinach or lettuce is worth trying. You can easily grow your own algae supply by placing a container of seawater in a location that gets some direct sunlight every day.

It is a good idea to offer your animals as varied a menu as possible at the beginning; you will soon learn the particular preferences of each kind of animal. Feed them once or twice a day. Don't worry about overfeeding them—they will stop eating when they have had enough. But be sure to remove uneaten scraps in the aquarium about fifteen minutes after feeding time, to prevent water fouling.

CALICO CRAB

SEA HORSE

Keeping your aquarium animals healthy

Ocean animals are sensitive to changes in water salinity, and so it is important to replace water lost through evaporation. When you first set up your aquarium, mark the exact water level on the glass side with a grease pencil or a bit of tape. Then, when the water level falls below the mark, bring it up again by adding distilled water, rain water, or even soft tap water that has been allowed to stand for a day or two. (For more precise control of salinity, you may wish to invest in a measuring instrument known as a *hydrometer,* available at pet stores for less than a dollar.)

The temperature of the water is important, too. Generally speaking, marine organisms require a cooler environment than do ordinary aquarium fishes. An average temperature of sixty-five degrees is about right, although most animals will stand seventy or even seventy-five degrees without much discomfort. In cold weather, keep the temperature from going below sixty degrees by using an all-glass, thermostatically controlled aquarium heater. In all cases, avoid any sudden change in temperature in either direction.

Dead or sick animals should be removed from the aquarium at once. Droppings, unconsumed food, and other detritus can be picked up with a dip tube. An occasional partial change of water (about ten percent every two weeks) has a tonic effect on the inhabitants. Before adding new animals to a healthy aquarium, "quarantine" them in a separate container for a few days to make sure they are free of disease.

With just a few minutes of care each day, your aquarium can be maintained for months or even years as a thriving miniature ocean community right in your home.

OCTOPUS

SAND DOLLAR

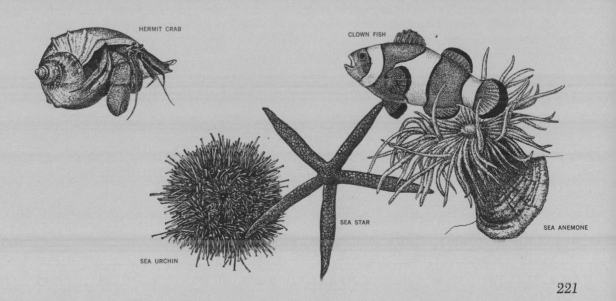

HERMIT CRAB

CLOWN FISH

SEA STAR

SEA ANEMONE

SEA URCHIN

221

A Walk along the Shore

1

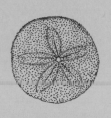

2

3

4

Most of us who are interested in the ocean and its life will never have a chance to explore its depths in a submarine or a bathyscaphe, yet anyone who has access to a seashore will find enough marine life to keep him interested and occupied for a lifetime. It is a simple matter to set yourself up as an amateur marine biologist: no license or diploma is required, and the equipment you need is neither complicated nor expensive.

Indeed, you can observe a fair amount of sea life without even getting your feet wet, simply by walking along a beach and picking through the wrack that marks the high-tide line. A few of the remains you may find there are shown in the margins of these two pages, and below are the living animals that produced them.

Any piece of timber tossed up on the beach, if it had spent much time in the water, is almost certain to show shipworm damage (1). The shipworm (which is not a worm but a burrowing clam called *Teredo*) has plagued mankind since the first savage lashed together the first raft and put out to sea.

Sand-dollar shells (2) are common along most shores. In life, this shell is covered with a velvety coating of fine spines. The five petal-shaped regions on the upper surface are the areas perforated by the animal's respiratory apparatus. Shake the shell —the rattling you hear is caused by five teeth left inside.

The long string of parchmentlike disks (3) is an empty egg case of one of the large whelks. The peculiar sand collar (4) is also an egg case—of the moon snail, which deposits its eggs in this formation of sand and jellylike mucus. The collar normally stays under the bottom sand, but it sometimes becomes dislodged and is washed ashore.

The skeleton of a sea urchin (5), denuded of the characteristic spines, bears little resemblance to the bristling living creature. The five-rayed design on the skeleton attests to the urchin's relationship to the sand dollar—and to the starfish, too, many of which have five arms.

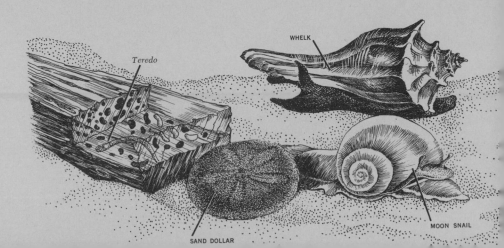

Teredo

WHELK

SAND DOLLAR

MOON SNAIL

Any oyster shell (6) cast up on the shore is likely to show a number of small, perfectly round holes. These are the work of the oyster drill, a small whelk that ranks with the starfish as an enemy of the oyster bed and attacks clams, mussels, and other shelled animals as well. Using a ribbon of closely set teeth, the whelk rasps a neat hole through the oyster's hard shell and then feasts on the soft tissue within.

You can usually pick up a number of different shells along a sandy beach, particularly if you visit it just after a storm. Most shells, unfortunately, rapidly lose their beautiful coloration when exposed to sunlight, air, and abrasive sand. This is true of the tulip shells (7), which belong to the largest marine snails found in American waters. The largest of the group, the Florida horse conch, can produce a shell up to two feet long. By contrast, the little cowrie shell (8), distinguished by the toothed lips on the underside, seldom exceeds an inch or two. In life, however, the cowrie makes up for its small size by displaying a beautifully patterned mantle that nearly covers the smooth, oval shell.

But watching living ocean animals is much more interesting than looking at the remains of dead ones, and requires little extra effort or equipment. If your shore includes tide pools or sheltered shallows, a glass-bottomed box or bucket will greatly add to your pleasure. (Try visiting these sites at night, too, with the aid of a waterproof flashlight—the difference in animal activity may surprise you.) If you turn over stones to see what's under them, remember to put them back in place when you're done—a good naturalist disturbs a habitat as little as possible.

Other equipment you may want includes a hand lens, a small spade or trowel for digging in sand or mudflats, and a quart jar or small white-bottomed pan in which to inspect animals more closely. To help in identifying the things you see and to add to your knowledge of them, a number of handbooks are available, including some excellent paperback ones that cost less than a dollar. (See the listing on page 227.)

With this simple equipment, you can become acquainted with hundreds of different ocean plants and animals, each with its own fascinating story to unfold.

5

6

7

8

OYSTER

COWRIE

SEA URCHIN

TULIP SHELL

Glossary

Abyss: The deep reaches of the ocean, beyond the relatively shallow *continental shelf*. The deepest parts of the abyss are its trenches, some of which descend to nearly seven miles below the surface.

Air bladder: The gas-filled sac that regulates a fish's buoyancy so that it may remain at a given level in the water without the effort of swimming. The sac, also called a swim bladder, is present in most bony fishes.

Alga (plural *algae*): The simplest of all plant forms, having neither roots, stems, nor leaves. Algae range in size from the microscopic *diatoms* to the large seaweeds that reach a hundred feet or more in length. *See also* Frond; Holdfast.

Bioluminescence: The production of light by a living organism, by means of a complex series of internal chemical reactions. Bioluminescence is displayed by a wide range of marine animals, from the single-celled *dinoflagellates* to many fishes and squid.

Bivalve: Possessing a two-part hinged shell. Bivalve *mollusks* include oysters, clams, and similar animals.

Calcareous: Formed of calcium carbonate, or lime—a common building material among ocean organisms, including the corals and the shelled *mollusks*.

Chlorophyll: A group of pigments that produces the green color of plants; essential to *photosynthesis*.

Chloroplast: A *chlorophyll*-bearing body within a plant cell in which *photosynthesis* takes place.

Cilia (singular *cilium*): Minute hairlike structures used for locomotion by many microscopic organisms.

Continental shelf: The bottom of the relatively shallow seas fringing the land masses. It ends where the bottom drops off abruptly to the great depths of the *abyss*. The shelf may vary from a few miles to a hundred or more in width.

Convection current: A movement in a liquid or a gas caused by differences in density.

Copepods: A group of *crustaceans* with rounded bodies and oarlike swimming antennae. Many copepod species occur in the *plankton*, forming important links in ocean *food chains*.

Crustacean: A member of the large group of animals that includes lobsters, crabs, barnacles, *copepods*, and similar forms. Crustaceans are characterized by jointed legs, a segmented body, and a hard external skeleton.

Current rip: The line of division between two water currents differing in speed, temperature, mineral content, or other characteristics. Current rips are often rich in planktonic life.

Detritus: Minute particles of the decaying remains of dead plants and animals; an important source of food for many marine animals.

Diatom: A single-celled *alga* encased in an intricately etched silica shell formed of two halves that fit together like a lid on a box.

Dinoflagellate: A member of a group of single-celled organisms that possess characteristics of both plants and animals. Like plants, some dinoflagellates can manufacture food through *photosynthesis*; like animals, some are capable of moving about and capturing prey.

Doldrums: An area of the ocean near the

equator where sailing ships were often be-calmed, owing to the lack of steady winds.

Ecology: The scientific study of the relationships of living things to one another and to their environment. The scientist who studies these relationships is an ecologist.

Elver: An immature eel, midway between the *Leptocephalus* stage and the adult form.

Flagellum (plural *flagella*): A whiplike structure used for locomotion by many single-celled organisms, such as the *dinoflagellates*.

Food chain: A series of plants and animals linked by their food relationships. *Plankton*, a plankton-eating fish, and a fish-eating bird would form a simple food chain. Any one species is normally represented in many different food chains. *See also* Food pyramid.

Food pyramid: Another way of representing a *food chain*, to take into consideration the volume of food consumed by each link in the chain. A simple food pyramid would show a hundred pounds of *plankton* producing ten pounds of plankton-eating fish, in turn producing one pound of fish-eating bird.

Foraminifera: A group of single-celled animals that form protective shells of lime. Chalk deposits are composed chiefly of vast numbers of these shells. *See also* Radiolaria.

Frond: The leaflike body of a seaweed.

Holdfast: The rootlike base of a marine *alga*. It anchors the plant to rocks or other surfaces but has no specific adaptations for absorbing water or nutrients.

Invertebrate: An animal without a backbone; the so-called "lower animals." *See also* Vertebrate.

Larva (plural *larvae*): An immature animal whose form differs from the adult form, such as the planktonic swimming stages of many bottom-dwelling *mollusks* and *crustaceans*.

Leptocephalus: The larval form of the eel, which transforms into an elver and ultimately becomes an adult eel.

Megalops: A late larval stage in the development of certain *crustaceans*, intermediate between the *zoea* stage and the adult form.

Mollusk: Any of a large group of *invertebrate* animals characterized by a soft unsegmented body usually, but not always, protected by a *calcareous* shell. Among the marine mollusks are the oyster, clam, mussel, squid, and octopus.

Mud line: On the ocean floor, the line of division between the sandy or gravelly bottom of the shallow waters and the finely divided deposits of the deeper waters.

Nauplius: The first larval stage of many *crustaceans*, characterized by three pairs of appendages and a single eye.

Nekton: *Pelagic* organisms capable of active swimming, such as the fishes and the whales. *See also* Plankton.

Ocellus (plural *ocelli*): A simple light-sensitive organ found in many *invertebrates*; a primitive eye.

Otocyst: An organ of balance found in some *invertebrates*, consisting of a fluid-filled sac with tiny lime granules which stimulate sensory cells when the animal moves. It is comparable to the inner ear of *vertebrates*.

Pelagic: Inhabiting the open water of the ocean, rather than the bottom or the shore. Pelagic plants and animals are divided into *plankton* and *nekton*.

Photophore: The light-producing organ of an animal. *See also* Bioluminescence.

Photosynthesis: The process by which green plants convert carbon dioxide and water into simple sugar. *Chlorophyll* and sunlight are essential to the series of complex chemical reactions involved.

Phytoplankton: Plant *plankton*. *See also* Zooplankton.

Plankton: The microscopic and near-microscopic plants (*phytoplankton*) and animals (*zooplankton*) that passively drift or float near the surface of a body of water. Plankton is of great ecological importance, directly or indirectly providing food for all other ocean life. *See also* Nekton.

Predator: An animal that lives by capturing other animals for food.

Radiolaria: A group of single-celled animals that form protective shells of silica. *See also* Foraminifera.

Thermocline: The dividing plane between two layers of water of different temperatures.

Trade winds: The relatively steady winds blowing toward the equator in a generally easterly direction from both the Southern and the Northern Hemispheres.

Veliger: The free-swimming larval form of many marine *mollusks*.

Vertebrate: An animal with a backbone. The vertebrates comprise fishes, amphibians, reptiles, birds, and mammals. *See also* Invertebrate.

Viscosity: The property of a liquid to resist the free movement of a body through it. The viscosity of seawater is an important factor in keeping many planktonic organisms afloat.

West Wind Drift: A system of eastward-flowing water currents that encircle the Antarctic continent.

Zoea: An early, free-swimming larval stage in the development of many *crustaceans*. *See also* Megalops.

Zooplankton: Animal *plankton*. *See also* Phytoplankton.

Bibliography

ANIMALS

ABBOTT, R. TUCKER. *American Seashells*. Van Nostrand, 1954.

BREDER, CHARLES M., JR. *Field Book of Marine Fishes of the Atlantic Coast*. Putnam, 1948.

BUCHSBAUM, RALPH. *Animals Without Backbones*. University of Chicago Press, 1948.

BUCHSBAUM, RALPH, and LORUS J. MILNE. *The Lower Animals*. Doubleday, 1961.

BUDKER, PAUL. *Whales and Whaling*. Macmillan, 1959.

BURT, WILLIAM HENRY. *A Field Guide to the Mammals*. Houghton Mifflin, 1964.

CURTIS, BRIAN. *The Life Story of the Fish*. Dover, 1949.

HERALD, EARL S. *Living Fishes of the World*. Doubleday, 1961.

HYMAN, LIBBIE H. *The Invertebrates* (five volumes). McGraw-Hill, 1940–1959.

MACGINITIE, GEORGE E., and NETTIE MACGINITIE. *Natural History of Marine Animals*. McGraw-Hill, 1949.

MINER, ROY WALDO. *Field Book of Seashore Life*. Putnam, 1950.

NATIONAL GEOGRAPHIC SOCIETY. *Wondrous World of Fishes*. National Geographic Society, 1965.

NORMAN, J. R. *A History of Fishes*. Hill and Wang.

NORMAN, J. R., and F. C. FRASER. *Field Book of Giant Fishes*. Putnam, 1949.

PETERSON, ROGER TORY. *A Field Guide to the Birds*. Houghton Mifflin, 1947.

PETERSON, ROGER TORY. *A Field Guide to Western Birds*. Houghton Mifflin, 1961.

ROMER, ALFRED S. *The Vertebrate Story*. University of Chicago Press, 1959.

SCHULTZ, LEONARD P., with EDITH M. STERN. *The Ways of Fishes*. Van Nostrand, 1948.

ZIM, HERBERT S., and HURST H. SHOEMAKER. *Fishes*. Golden Press, 1957.

PLANKTON

DAVIS, CHARLES C. *The Marine and Fresh-water Plankton*. Michigan State University Press, 1955.

HARDY, SIR ALISTER. *The Open Sea: Its Natural History*. Houghton Mifflin, 1956.

PLANTS

SMITH, GILBERT M. *Marine Algae of the Monterey Peninsula, California*. Stanford University Press, 1944.

TAYLOR, WILLIAM R. *Marine Algae of the Northeastern Coast of North America*. University of Michigan Press, 1957.

MARINE BIOLOGY

BUZZATI-TRAVERSO, A. A. (Editor). *Perspectives in Marine Biology*. University of California Press, 1960.

EVANS, I. O. (Editor). *Sea and Seashore*. Warne, 1962.

JÄGERSTEN, GOSTA. *Life in the Sea*. Basic Books, 1964.

MARSHALL, N. B. *Aspects of Deep Sea Biology*. Philosophical Library, 1954.

WALFORD, LIONEL A. *Living Resources of the Sea*. The Ronald Press, 1958.

ECOLOGY

ALLEE, WARDER C., and others. *Principles of Animal Ecology*. Saunders, 1949.

BUCHSBAUM, RALPH, and MILDRED BUCHSBAUM. *Basic Ecology*. Boxwood Press, 1957.

FARB, PETER, and THE EDITORS OF LIFE. *Ecology*. Time, Inc., 1963.

MOORE, HILARY B. *Marine Ecology*. Wiley, 1958.

ODUM, EUGENE P., and HOWARD T. ODUM. *Fundamentals of Ecology*. Saunders, 1959.

OCEANOGRAPHY

CAIDIN, MARTIN. *Hydrospace*. Dutton, 1964.

COKER, R. E. *This Great and Wide Sea*. University of North Carolina Press, 1947.

COWEN, ROBERT C. *Frontiers of the Sea*. Doubleday, 1963.

GASKELL, T. F. *World Beneath the Oceans*. Natural History Press, 1964.

PETTERSSON, HANS. *The Ocean Floor*. Yale University Press, 1954.

RUSSELL, FREDERICK S., and C. M. YONGE. *The Seas*. Warne, 1963.

SEARS, MARY (Editor). *Oceanography*. American Association for the Advancement of Science, 1961.

STOMMEL, HENRY. *The Gulf Stream*. University of California Press, 1958.

SVERDRUP, H. U., MARTIN W. JOHNSON, and RICHARD H. FLEMING. *The Oceans*. Prentice-Hall, 1942.

GENERAL READING

BERRILL, N. J. *The Living Tide*. Dodd, Mead, 1951.

BERRILL, N. J., and JACQUELYN BERRILL. *1001 Questions Answered about the Seashore*. Dodd, Mead, 1959.

BUTCHER, DEVEREUX. *Exploring Our National Parks and Monuments*. Houghton Mifflin, 1960.

BUTCHER, DEVEREUX. *Exploring Our National Wild Life Refuges*. Houghton Mifflin, 1963.

CARRINGTON, RICHARD. *A Biography of the Sea*. Basic Books, 1960.

CARSON, RACHEL. *The Edge of the Sea*. Houghton Mifflin, 1955.

CARSON, RACHEL. *The Sea Around Us*. Oxford University Press, 1961.

CLARKE, ARTHUR C. *The Challenge of the Sea*. Holt, Rinehart and Winston, 1960.

ENGEL, LEONARD, and THE EDITORS OF LIFE. *The Sea*. Time, Inc., 1961.

RAY, CARLETON, and ELGIN CIAMPI. *The Underwater Guide to Marine Life*. A. S. Barnes, 1956.

ZIM, HERBERT S., and LESTER INGLE. *Seashores*. Golden Press, 1955.

Illustration Credits and Acknowledgments

COVER: Red grouper, Douglas Faulkner

ENDPAPERS: Waves, Douglas Faulkner

UNCAPTIONED PHOTOGRAPHS: *8–9:* White-tailed tropicbird, Sandy Sprunt from National Audubon Society *44–45:* School of immature fish, Douglas Faulkner *104–105:* Unloading the catch, N. J. Berrill *138–139:* Diver in kelp bed, Ralph J. Nelson II

ALL OTHER ILLUSTRATIONS: *10–11:* Howard Cleaves from National Audubon Society *12–13:* Charles Fracé *14–16:* Karl W. Kenyon *17:* Russ Kinne from Photo Researchers *18:* Victor De Palma from F.P.G. *19:* Harold E. Edgerton *20:* Keith Gillett *21:* Robert C. Hermes *22–23:* Felix Cooper *24:* Patricia C. Henrichs *25:* George Lower *26:* Robert C. Hermes from National Audubon Society *27:* Douglas Faulkner *28:* Patricia C. Henrichs *29:* Felix Cooper *30:* D. P. Wilson *31:* Mark A. Binn *32–33:* Douglas Faulkner *34:* N.A.S.A. *36–37:* Thase Daniel *38–39:* William M. Stephens *40:* Peter David *41:* William H. Amos *42–43:* Roger Tory Peterson from Photo Researchers *46–47:* Patricia C. Henrichs *48–49:* Walter Dawn *50:* D. P. Wilson *51:* Patricia C. Henrichs *52–53:* Hans Zillessen from G.A.I. *54–55:* Hans Zillessen from G.A.I. (after Hardy) *56:* D. P. Wilson; William H. Amos *57:* Patricia C. Henrichs *58–59:* Robert C. Hermes from National Audubon Society *60:* N. J. Berrill *61:* Douglas Faulkner *62:* Ralph J. Nelson II *64:* Peter David *65:* Douglas Faulkner *66:* William H. Amos *67:* Walter A. Starck II *68–69:* Constance P. Warner *70–71:* Mark A. Binn (after Hardy) *72–73:* Charles Fracé *74:* Edmund S. Hobson *75:* Russ Kinne from Photo Researchers; Michael A. de Camp *76–77:* Edmund S. Hobson *78–79:* Michael A. de Camp, courtesy of Blue Meridian, Inc., New York, N.Y. *80:* Dennis Hallinan from F.P.G. *81–82:* Mark A. Binn *83:* Shostal *84–87:* Merrill P. Spencer *88–89:* Hans Zillessen from G.A.I. (after Russell) *90:* D. P. Wilson *91:* Felix Cooper *92–99:* Peter David *100–101:* Hans Zillessen from G.A.I. *102:* Ralph J.

Nelson II *106:* Patricia C. Henrichs *107–109:* D. P. Wilson *110:* Charles Fracé *111:* Mark A. Binn *112:* Ernest Gay *113:* Karl W. Kenyon *114–119:* Dr. Carleton Ray, New York Zoological Society *120–121:* Hans Zillessen from G.A.I. *122:* D. Richard Statile *123:* Hans Zillessen from G.A.I. *124:* National Institute of Oceanography, Wormley, England *125:* D. Richard Statile *126–129:* Dr. Carleton Ray, New York Zoological Society *130–131:* Hans Zillessen from G.A.I. *132:* J. B. Nelson *133:* Mark A. Binn *134:* Hans Zillessen from G.A.I. *135:* Louis Renault from Photo Researchers *136–137:* M. Woodbridge Williams *140:* Patricia C. Henrichs *141:* Don Wobber *143:* Coles Phinizy *144:* Ralph J. Nelson II *145:* Karl W. Kenyon *146–147:* Walter A. Starck II *148–149:* L. T. Grigg from F.P.G. *150–155:* Douglas Faulkner *156:* Mark A. Binn *156–157:* Keith Gillett *158–159:* Douglas Faulkner *160–163:* Elgin Ciampi *164–173:* Douglas Faulkner *174:* L. T. Grigg from F.P.G. *175:* Keith Gillett *176:* Douglas Faulkner *177:* Mark A. Binn *178–179:* Douglas Faulkner *180–181:* Patricia C. Henrichs *182–184:* D. P. Wilson *185:* Patricia C. Henrichs *186:* United States Air Force *187:* Charles Fracé *188:* D. P. Wilson *189:* Charles Fracé *190:* Patricia C. Henrichs *191:* William H. Amos *192:* Patricia C. Henrichs (after Chun) *193–194:* United States Navy Electronics Laboratory *196–197:* Graphic Arts International *198:* P. Berger *201:* Patricia C. Henrichs *202–213:* Charles Fracé *214–216:* Mark A. Binn *217–221:* Charles Fracé *222–223:* Patricia C. Henrichs

PHOTO EDITOR: ROBERT J. WOODWARD

ACKNOWLEDGMENTS: *The publisher wishes to thank William Perry and Boyd Evison of the National Park Service, both of whom read the entire manuscript and offered valuable suggestions. The assistance of Professor Vladim D. Vladykov of the University of Ottawa and of Lt. Risdon S. Wood, Navy Representative, Office of the Assistant Secretary of Defense, United States Department of Defense, is also appreciated.*

Index

[Page numbers in **boldface** type indicate reference to illustrations.]

Abalones, 142, 145
Abyss, defined, 224
  (*See also* Depth)
Acadia National Park (Maine), 202
Acartia (copepods), **54**
Acorn barnacles, **180**
  larvae of, 106, **108–109**
Acorn worms, 195
Adélie penguins, **127**, 128
Air bladders, of fish, **70**, 71, 224
  of seaweeds, **24**, **46**
Albatrosses, 12, **13**, 113, 128
Aleutian Islands, **113**, 142, 144
Algae, brown (kelp), 140–145, 177
  coralline, 140, 164, 177
  defined, 224
  (*See also* Diatoms)
Amber jacks, 37
Amphiprion (clown fish), 219, 221
Anchovies, 133–134
Andes Mountains, 165
Anemones, sea, 37, **141**, 142, 148–149,
  166, 189, 219, **221**
Angler fish, **73**, 97, 100
Animals, 45–46, 139
  as deep scattering layer, 101–103
  deep-sea, 91–93
  endangered, **206–207**
  transparent (*see* Transparent animals)
  (*See also* Birds; Breeding; Copepods;
  Coral reefs; Crustaceans; Dinoflagel-
  lates; Fish; Migration; Mollusks; Plank-
  ton; Whales; *specific animals*)
Antarctic Circle, 106
Antarctic Ocean, 11, 103, 113–131, 134,
  195
  currents of, 20, *map* **22–23**, 91, 113,
  130–131
  life pyramid in, 118–121
  penguins in, 127–129
  sea pastures in, 114–115
  upwelling in, 130–131
  whales in, 123–126
Antler coral, **162–163**
Aquaculture, 214
Aquariums, home, **217–221**
Arctic Circle, 106
Arctic Ocean, 103, 124, 131, 195
Arcturus, the, **36**, 37
Armored flagellates (*see* Dinoflagellates)
Arrowworms, 60, **90**
Ascidians (*see* Sea squirts)
Ascophyllum (knotted wrack), **46**
Asterias (starfish), 183
Atlantic harbor porpoises, **81**
Atlantic Ocean, 74–75, 88, 131
  baleen whales of, 123, 124
  birds of, 10–11, 13
  currents of, 21, *map* **22–23**, 155
  kelp beds in, 140, 142
  Sargasso Sea in, 24, 26, 29
Atlantic right whales, 123, **207**
Atomic explosions, 186–187
Australian Currents, *map* **22–23**
Autumn, 110–111
Amver, the, 50

Baja California, 82
Baleen whales, 119, **121–122**, 123–126
  (*See also* Hump-backed whales)
Barnacles, 26, 40, 57, **141**, **180**
  filter technique of, 181–182
  larvae of, **54–55**, 106, **108–109**
Barracudas, **158**, 166
Basking sharks, 74–75, **209**
Beagle, the, 50, 140
Beebe, William, 36–37, 41, 60, 91
Benguela Current, *map* **22–23**, 152
Bering Sea, *map* **82**
Beroe (comb jellies), **61**
Bikini Atoll, **186**
Bioluminescence, 50–51, 95–100, 224
Birds, 37, 40, 74, 132–137, 141
  Antarctic, 113–115, 118
  winds and, 9–18
  (*See also specific birds*)
Biscayne Bay National Monument
  (Florida), 202–203
Bivalve, defined, 224
Bladders, air (*see* Air bladders)
  swim, 103
Blennies, **179**
Blubber, 117, **125**
Blue marlins, **205**
Blue Meridian Diver's Elevator, **78–79**
Blue sharks, 74, **75**, **208**
Blue tangs, 168–169
Blue whales, **81**, 123–126, **213**
Bonitos, 18, 74, 134
Bony fish, 46, 70–74, 190
  (*See also specific bony fish*)
Boobies, 14, 16–18, 37, **42–43**, **132**, **134**
Botryllus (golden stars), 141
Bottle-nosed dolphins, **80–81**, **213**
Bottom, ocean (*see* Floor, ocean)
Brachiopods, 181
Brain coral, 148, **151**, 155, **163**
Brazil Current, *map* **22–23**
Breeding, 142, 145, 160, 190
  of crustaceans, 56–57
  of eels, 28–29
  of flying fish, 26
  of herring, 54–55
  of petrels, 11
  of plaice, 30–31
  of whales, 82, 124–126
  (*See also* Larval stage)
Brill, 31
Bristle worms, **108–109**, 166
Brittle stars, 166, **184**, 185, 189, **194**, 195
Brown pelicans, **135**
Buck Island Reef National Monument
  (Virgin Islands), **160–163**, 202–203
Burrowers, 187–189, 192, 195
Butterfly fish, **73**

Cabrillo National Monument (California),
  map **82**, 203
Cactus coral, 155
Calanus (copepods), 53–55, 90, 106–107,
  115, 124
Calcareous, defined, 224

Calcareous (coralline) algae, 140, 164,
  177
Calcareous shells, 51
Calico crabs, **220**
California Current, *map* **22**
California gray whales, 82, **83**, **207**
California sea lions, **211**
California sea otters, **144–145**
Camera-type eyes, 93–95
Camouflage, 26, **32–33**, 67, 92
  (*See also* Pigmentation)
Canaries Current, *map* **22–23**, 24
Cape Cod National Seashore (Massachu-
  setts), 203
Cape Hatteras, 11
Cape Hatteras National Seashore (North
  Carolina), 203–204
Carbohydrates, 149
Carbon dioxide, 149
Caribbean Sea, 21, 155, 158–166
Carinaria (snails), **66**
Cephalopod eyes, **68**
Ceratium (dinoflagellates), **50**
Chaetoceros (diatoms), **49**
Chalk deposits, 195, **198**, 199
Challenger Deep, 214–215
Challenger expedition, 195
Channel Islands National Monument
  (California), 204
Chlorophyll, 50–51, 224
Chloroplasts, 47, 224
Chordata, 64, 165
Chromatophores, **32–33**
Cilia, 57–58, 224
Clam worms, **189**
Clams, 40–41, 56, 106, 185–187, 189
  coral-reef, 156, **174–175**
  in kelp beds, 142, 145
Cleaning fish, **178–179**
Clown fish, 219, **221**
Cobalt, 186–187
Cod, 35, 186, 189
Colorado River, **34**
Coloration (*see* Pigmentation)
Columbus, Christopher, 24, 41
Comb jellies, **60–61**, 65, 94
Common skates, **210**
Conches, 158
Conshelf III, **216**
Continental shelf, 88, **130–131**, 139, 177–
  192, 224
  radioactivity and, 186–187
Convection currents, **130–131**, 224
Copepods, 53–55, 57, 88–90, 106–109,
  124, 133, 224
  Antarctic, 114–115
Coquina clams, **185**
Coral reefs, 72, 145–179, **186**
  locations of, 152, 155
  in public parks, 155, 158, 160–166,
  202–203
Coralline algae, 140, 164, 177
Coriolis force, 23
Cormorants, **134–135**
Corneas, **69**
Cousteau, Jacques-Yves, 216

Cowrie shells, **223**
Crabeater seals, **118**, 119
Crabs, **25**, 26, 41, 158, 179, 189, 195
  for aquariums, 219–221
  in kelp beds, 140, 142, 145
  larvae of, **56**, 57
Crawfish, 57
Creepers, 180, 187–188, 192
Crinoidea, 164
Crustaceans, 47, 49, 103, 134, 136, 140, 224
  Antarctic, 91, 114–115, 126
  (*See also* Barnacles; Copepods; Crabs; Krill; Lobsters; Shrimp)
Currents, 20–24, 42–43, 112–113, 133, 137, 139–140
  migration and, 35, 90–91
  on ocean floor, 180–181
  rips of, 36–41, 43, 133, 224
  types of, 20–21
  upwelling of, **130–131**, 135–136
  (*See also specific currents*)
Cuttlefish, 97, 103
Cytoplasm, **106**

Dactylometra (jellyfish), **58–59**
Daisy coral, **150**
Dampier, William, 21
Darwin, Charles, 50, 140–141
Decapod larvae, **55**
Deep scattering layer, 100–103
Deepstar 4000, 214, 216
Deposit feeders, 180, 187–188
Depth, ocean, 88, 192–195, 199, 214–216
  sounding of, **100**, 101, 103
  (*See also* Abyss)
Deserts, sea, 113–114
Detritus, 180, 185, 187, 224
Devilfish (manta rays), 74–75, **76–77**, 137, **210**
Diatoms, 47–56, 58, 89, **106–110**, 224
  Antarctic, 114–115, 118–121, 125
  in Humboldt Current, 133, **134**, 136
  ooze derived from, 195, *map* **196–197**
  reproduction of, **106**
Dinoflagellates, **50**, 51, **54–55**, 95, 106, 224
  Antarctic, 114
  coral-reef, 149, 158
  in Humboldt Current, 133, **134**, 136
Divers, **78–79**, **116**, 141, 158, **162–163**
Doldrums, 20–21, 224–225
Dolphin fish, 40, 74, 137
Dolphins, 18, **36–37**, **80–81**, 211, **213**
Dorsal fins, **70–71**, **85**
Drag, 46
Drake, Sir Francis, 18, 105
Driftwood, 40, **41**, 43

Earth's rotation, 22–23
East Australian Current, *map* **22–23**
Echo sounding, **100**, 101, 103
Ecology, defined, 225
Eelgrass, 72
Eels, 28–30, 35, **55**, **73**
  in coral reefs, 158, **159**, 176, **179**
El Niño, 136
Elephant seals, **212**
Elephant's-tusks, **187**, 188
Elkhorn coral, **146–147**
Elvers, **28**, 29, 225
Emperor grammas, **171**
Emperor penguins, 128, **129**
Equator, 10, 12, 134–135, 155
Equatorial Countercurrent, *map* **22**
Equatorial Currents, 20–24, 42–43, 133
Euphausids, **51**, 91, 97
Everglades National Park (Florida), **204**
Evolution, 68–69, 72

Eyes, 174, 183
  of deep-sea creatures, 93–95, 97
  evolution of, **68–69**
  of flatfish, 30–31

Faeroes, 28
Fairy bass, **170**
False bottom, 100–103
Faulkner, Doug, **179**
Feather stars, **164**, 166
Fertilizer, natural (guano), 133, 135
Fertilizer (nutrient) salts, 110–112, 114, 130–131, 135, 149
Filefish, **72**
Filter feeders, 180–182, 185–187
Fin-backed whales, 123–124
Finger coral, 155
Fins, of fish, **70–71**
Fish, 66–75, 101, 189
  Antarctic, 115, **120**, 128
  body parts of, **70–71**
  bony, 46, 70–74, 190
  coral-reef, 149, 156, 158, 166, **168–173**, **178–179**
  deep-sea, 93, 95–100
  in Humboldt Current, 133–134
  in kelp forests, 140–143
  migration of, 28–35
  mollusks and, 66–67
  in red tide, **136–137**
  (*See also specific fishes*)
Flagellates, armored (*see* Dinoflagellates)
Flagellum, defined, 224
Flamingo-tongue snails, 166 ·
Flatfish, **30–33**, **72**, 189
Flatworms, 26, 166
Fletcher, Francis, 18
Floor, ocean, 45, 66, 74–75, 131, 139–199
  contours of, 22, 101, 195
  coral reefs on, 72, 145–179, **186**
  darkness on, 91
  false, 100–103
  kelp beds on, 140–145
  sediments on, 35, 155, 180, 192, 195–199
  (*See also* Continental shelf; Depth)
Flounder, 31–33, 189
Flower coral, 155
Flying fish, 15, **18–19**, 26, 71, **72**, 137
Food chains, **52–55**, 115, 225
  (*See also* Food pyramid)
Food pyramid, 118–121, 133–134, 136, 225
Foraminifera, **51**, 195, 225
Fort Jefferson National Monument (Florida), 204
Fresh water, 35, 155
  (*See also* Rainfall)
Frigatebirds, 13–17, 37, 160
Frond, defined, 225
Fungus coral, 155

Galápagos iguana, **42–43**
Galápagos Islands, 16, 42–43
Garibaldis, **143**
Gas chambers, of animals, 103, 192
Gemini IV, 35
Gentoo penguins, 128
Giant clams, 156, **174–175**
Giant manta rays, 74–75, **76–77**, 137, **210**
Gill rakers, 55, 134
Gills, **70**, 181
Gimbel, Peter, **78**
Girdle of Venus, 60
Glass sponges, 192
Glaucus (sea slugs), 37–39
Globigerina (foraminiferan), **51**, 195
Globigerina ooze, 195–199
Glossodoris (nudibranch), **167**
Goatfish, **178**

Golden Hind, the, 18, 105
Goniopora (daisy coral), **150**
Gravel, 139, 185, 196
Gravity, 177, 180
Gray whales, California, 82–83, **207**
Great Barrier Reef (Australia), 155–157
Great Ice Barrier, 128
Green turtles, **206**
Griffin, Edward I., 84, **86**
Groupers, **171**
Guano, 133, 135
Gulf of Maine, 53
Gulf of Mexico, 21, 26, **34**, 155
Gulf Stream, 21, *map* **22**, 24, 26, 155
Gulls, 9
Gulpers, **73**

Haddock, 55, 189
Halibut, 189
Haliotis (abalones), 142, 145
Hammerhead sharks, 74, 137, **209**
Harbor seals, **212**
Hatteras, Cape, 11
Hawaiian shore, **112**
Hawkins, Richard, 59–60
Heart urchins, **188**
Heliosphaera (radiolarian), **51**
Hermit crabs, 142, 189, 219, **221**
Herring, 53–55, 70, 74, 88–89
Holdfast, defined, 225
Holothurians, 140
Horseshoe crabs, **203**
Humboldt Current, *map* **22**, 133–136, 152
Hump-backed whales, **81**, **121**, 123–124, 133
Hurricanes, 158
Hutton, J. W., 12
Hydrogen bomb tests, **186**, 187
Hydroids, 26, 141
Hydrometers, **219**, 221

Ianthina (snails), 37, **40**
Ice, Antarctic, **130–131**
Iguanas, Galápagos, **42–43**
Indian Countercurrent, *map* **23**
Indian Ocean, 13, 23, 174, 199
Ink of squids, 95
Invertebrate, defined, 225
Iridocytes, 33
Iris diaphragms, 69

Japan Current, *map* **23**
Jellyfish, 20, 45, 58–60, 63, 65, 72, **88–90**, 95, 115, 133, 141
John Pennekamp Coral Reef State Park (Florida), 155, 158, 164–166, 202–203

Kelp, 140–145, 177
Keratin, 190
Killer whales, **81**, **84–87**, 123, 144, **213**
  in food pyramid, 119–121
King penguins, 128
Knotted wrack, **46**
Kon-Tiki, 105
Koran angelfish, **171**
Krill, 114–115, 118–121, 123–125, 127–128

Labrador Current, *map* **22**
Labroides dimidiatus (wrasses), **178–179**
Laminaria (kelp), **140**
Lamp shells, **181**
Land barriers, 22–23
Lantern fish, **73**
Larva, defined, 225
Larval stage, 56–58, **108–109**, 165, 190
  of eels, **28**
  food chain and, **54–55**
  in springtime, 106–107
Lenses, eye, 69, 95

Leopard seals, **119**
Leptocephalus brevirostris, **28**, 225
Life, pyramid of, 118–121, 133–134, 136
Light, 45–46, 49–51, 69
 for kelp beds, 140
 ocean depth and, 91–93, 95
 in photosynthesis, 50, 149, 158
 produced by deep-sea animals, 72,
  95–100, 192
 in springtime, 110–111
 vertical migration and, 88–91
Limpets, 140
Lionfish, **172–173**
Lizards, Galápagos, **42–43**
Lobsters, 56–57, 142, 189, **202**
Long Island, 78
Long-neck clams, 185–186
Lugworms, 187

McDivitt, James A., 35
Mackerel, 55, 70–71, **73**, 74
 (*See also* Tuna)
Magellan, Strait of, 140–141
Maine, Gulf of, 53
Mammals, **211–213**
 Antarctic, 118
 (*See also* Otters; Seals; Whales)
Man-eating sharks, 74
Man-of-war, Portuguese, **20**, 64
Man-of-war birds (frigatebirds) 13–17,
 37, 160
Manatees, **212**
Manta rays, 74–75, **76–77**, 137, **210**
Mariana Trench, 195
Masked boobies, **42–43**
Megalops, **56**, 57, 225
Mexico, Gulf of, 21, 26, **34**, 155
Middle ocean (twilight zone), 93, 97, 101
Migration, 101, 142
 of birds, 11–12
 of deep scattering layer, 100–101, 103
 of fish, 28–35
 of plankton, 88–91
 of whales, *map* **82**, 125
Milk of whales, 125–126
Millepora (coral), 164
Minerals, 22, 46, 110–112, 114, 133,
 214–215
 upwelling of, 130–131, 135
 (*See also* Salts)
Mississippi River, 155
Mollusks, 66–70, 95, 100, 140–142,
 187–188, 225
 (*See also specific mollusks*)
Monaco, 28
Moon snails, 189, 222
Moosehead coral, 155
Moray eels, **73**, 158, **159**, 176, **179**
"Mother Carey's chickens" (storm
 petrels), **10–12**
Mountains, sea, 101
Mud, 139, 187
 (*See also* Ooze; Silt)
Mud line, 192, 225
Mussels, 142, 182, 189
"Mustache whales," 125
Mycedium (coral), **150**
Mysid shrimp, 88–89
Mysticeti ("mustache whales"), 125

"Namu" (killer whale), **84–87**
Naples, Italy, 28
National Park Service, 160, 202
Nauplius larvae, 56–57, 225
Nekton, 66–67, 225
Nereis (clam worm), **189**
New York Zoological Society, 116
Niño, El (wind), 136
Nitrates, 110–111
Noctiluca (dinoflagellates), **50**, 51
North Atlantic Drift, *map* 22–23

North Equatorial Current, 21, *map* **22**, 24
North Pacific Current, *map* **22–23**
North Sea, 30
Nuclei, cell, **106**
Nutrient (fertilizer) salts, 110–112, 114,
 130–131, 135, 149

Obelia (jellyfish), **90**
Ocelli, 63, 225
Octopuses, **68**, 159, 174, **176–177**, 219,
 221
Olympic National Park (Washington), 204
Ooze, deep-sea, 192, 195–199
Opossum shrimp, 90, 133
Otocysts, 63, 225
Otters, sea, 141, **144–145, 206**
Oxygen, 149
Oysters, **180**, 182–183, **223**

Pacific Ocean, 35, 88, 124, 195, 199
 birds of, 13, 16–17
 coral reefs in, 156, 174
 currents of, 21, *map* **22–23**, 133–135
 kelp beds in, 140, 142, 144
Padre Island National Seashore (Texas),
 205
Parasitic fish, 100
Parrot fish, **163**
Pasture, sea (*see* Plankton)
Pelagia (jellyfish), **62**
Pelagic, defined, 225
Pelicans, 9, 134, **135**, 160, **204**
Penguins, 66–67, 113, 126–129, 134
Peruvian boobies, **132**
Peruvian cormorants, **135**
Peruvian (Humboldt) Current, *map* **22**,
 133–136, 152
Peruvian penguins, 134
Petrels, **114**
 storm, **10–12**
Phalaropes, 37
Phosphates, 110–111
Photography, underwater, 78, 103, 116,
 195
Photophores (light organs), 95–100, 225
Photosynthesis, 47, 149, 158, 225
Phyllosoma, 57
Physalia (Portuguese man-of-war), **20**, 64
Phytoplankton, 46–47, 53, 58, 89, **107**,
 225
 Antarctic, 114, 130
 (*See also* Diatoms; Dinoflagellates)
Picard, Jacques, 214–215
Pigmentation, 74–75, **92–93**, 148, 164,
 169–170, 174
 (*See also* Camouflage; Transparent
 animals)
Plaice, **30**, 31
Planarians, 140
Plankton (sea pasture), 47, 51–53, 56,
 100, 123, 180, 226
 absence of, 112
 Antarctic, 114–115, 118–121
 coral-reef, 166, 174
 in Humboldt Current, 133–134
 larvae in, 56–58
 nekton and, 66
 in ooze, 195–197
 springtime, 106–109
 vertical migration of, 88–91
 (*See also* Diatoms; Dinoflagellates;
 Phytoplankton)
Plants, 45–47, 139
 coral-reef, 149, 158, 166, 174
 (*See also* Diatoms; Dinoflagellates;
 Driftwood; Plankton; Seaweed;
 specific plants)
Plymouth, England, 28
Point Lobos, California, 144
Point Loma, California, 82

Point Reyes National Seashore
 (California), 205
Polyps, coral, 151
Porites (coral), 164
Porpita, **38–39**, 40
Porpoises, 54, 66, 74, **81**, 141, 211
Portuguese men-of-war, **20**, 64
Prawns, **92–93**, 95, 97
Predator, defined, 226
Pressure, water, 91, 192
Pseudocalanus (copepods), **54**
Pterophryne (sargassum fish), **26**
Pteropod ooze, *map* **196–197**, 199
Pteropods, 66, 199
Pyramid of life, 118–121, 133–134, 136
Pyrosomes, **65**

Quahog clams, **185**

Radioactivity, 186–187
Radiolaria, **51**, 52, 199, 226
Radiolarian ooze, *map* **196–197**, 199
Rainfall, 22, 158
Rakers, gill, 55, 134
Rays, 69, 71–72, 74–77, 137, 189, **210**
Razor shells, **185**, 186
Red clay deposits, *map* **196–197**
"Red feed," 53
Red Sea corals, **150**
Red tides, **136–137**
Reefs (*see* Coral reefs)
Reentrants, 211
Regeneration, 185
Rhizosolenia (diatoms), **48**
Right whales, 123, **207**
Rips, current, 36–41, 43, 133
River water, **34**, 35, 155
Rock hoppers, 128

Sailors by the wind, **20**, **21**, 40, 64
Salmon, Pacific, 35
Salps, **64**, 65, 133
Salts, mineral, 110–112, 114, 130–131,
 135, 149
Sand, 187–188, 196
Sand dollars, **221–222**
Sand eels, **55**
Sand sharks, **74–75**
Sargasso Sea, 24, 26, 29
Sargassum fish, **26**
Sargassum sea slugs, 26
Sargassum shrimp, 26, **27**
Sargassum weed, **24–27**, 46
Sawfish, **210**
Scallops, **181–183**
Scattering layer, deep, 100–103
Scavengers, 142, 189
Schmidt, Johannes, 28
Schooling of fish, 170
Sea anemones, 37, **141**, 142, 148–149,
 166, 189, 219, **221**
Sea biscuits, **188**
Sea butterflies, 66–67, 199
Sea cucumbers, **181**, 186, 195
Sea elephants, 145
Sea fans, 148–149, **152–153**, 165–166
Sea gooseberries, **60**
Sea gulls, 9
Sea horses, **72**, 219, **220**
Sea lilies, 192
Sea lions, 145, **211**
Sea mats, 26, 141
Sea nettles, **58–59**
Sea otters, 141, **144–145, 206**
Sea pasture (*see* Plankton)
Sea pens, 192
Sea rods, 148–149, 165
"Sea serpents," 64
Sea slugs, 26, 37–39, 140–141, 166
 (*See also* Snails)

Sea squirts (ascidians), 26, 65, 140–141, **165**, 166, **180**, 185
  in the deep sea, 192, 194
  filter technique of, 181–182, 186
Sea stars (*see* Starfish)
Sea turtles, 40, 43, 74, 158, 160
Sea urchins, 142, 145, 166, 174, **181**, 189, **193**, 222–223
  for aquariums, 219, **221**
  larvae of, 56–57
Sea whips, **154**
Sealab II, 216
Seals, 113, 115–120, 141, 145, **212**
Seasons, 105–112, 125, 142
Seattle, Washington, *map* **82**, 84
Seaweed, **24–27**, **46**, 148
  forests of, 140–145, 177
Sediment (silt), 35, 155, 180, *map* **196–197**
  (*See also* Ooze)
Sense organs, 63, 70–71, 182
  (*See also* Eyes)
Serpent (brittle) stars, 166, **184**, 185, 189, **194**, 195
Severn River (England), 28
Sharks, 40, 71–72, **74–75**, **78–79**, 137, 158, **208–209**
Shipworms, 40–41, **222**
Shrimp, 26–27, 88–90, 133, 142, 179, 189, 195
  (*See also* Prawns)
Silt, 35, 155, 180, 196
Siphonophores, 64–65, **102**, 103
  (*See also* Portuguese men-of-war; Sailors-by-the-wind)
Sitters, 180–182, 192
Skates, 71–72, 189–191, **210**
Skin divers, 141, 158, **162–163**
Skipjacks, **158**
Slugs, sea, 26, 37–39, 140–141, 166
  (*See also* Snails)
Snails, 37, **40**, 56, 66, 106, 189, 196, 222–223
  coral-reef, 156, **166**
  veliger larvae of, **57**, 58
  (*See also* Abalones; Slugs; Whelks)
Soft-shell clams, **185**
Sole, 31, 189
Sooty albatrosses, 128
Sounding, depth, **100**, 101, 103
South Equatorial Current, 21, *map* **22–23**, 133
Spawning (*see* Breeding)
Sperm whales, **81**, **213**
Sponges, 142, 166, **167**, 181, 192
Spring, 106–111, 125
Squid, 54, 66, **67–68**, 70, 92, 177

Squid, Antarctic, 115, 120
  eyes of, 93–95, 174
  light produced by, 95, **97**
Squirrelfish, **178**
Staghorn coral, 148, **155**
Stalked jellyfish, 141
Star coral, 155
Starfish, 140, 142, 156, **181–184**, 189, **221**
  larvae of, 56–57, 106
Stickiness (viscosity), 46, 67, 226
Sting rays, **69**, **210**
Stonefish, 156
Storm petrels, **10–12**
Strait of Magellan, 140–141
Strontium, 186–187
Sub-ice observation chambers ("SOC"), **116**
Sulphur-bottomed (blue) whales, **81**, 123–126, **213**
Summer, 107, 110–111, 125, 142
Sun stars, 189
Sunfish, ocean, **73**
Suspension feeders, 180, 182
Swim bladders, 103
Swimmers, 180, 183
Synapta, **187**

Tarpons, 71, 74
Telescopic eyes, **95**
Television, underwater, 103
Temora (copepods), **54**
Temperature, water, 91, 111
  of currents, 22, 133, 135–136
  of polar seas, 114, 116–117, 130–131
  tropical, 113–114, 152, 155
Teredo (shipworms), 40–41, **222**
Terns, 9
Terrigenous deposits, *map* **196–197**
Thermocline, defined, 226
Thresher sharks, 74–75, **209**
Tides, 22, **136–137**, 139–140
Tiger sharks, 74
Trade winds, 21, 23, 226
Transparent animals, **20–21**, **38–39**, 40, 58–65, 92
  (*See also* Jellyfish)
Trenches, ocean, 195
Tridacna (giant clams), 156, **174–175**
Trieste I, 103, 195, 214, **215**
Tripod fish, **73**
Tropic seas, 112–113, 199
  (*See also* Coral reefs)
Tropicbirds, 37
Tubeworms, 26
Tulip shells, **223**
Tuna, 52–54, 71, **73**, 74

Turbots, 31
Turtles, 40, 43, 74, 158, 160, **206**
Twilight zone, 93, 97, 101

Upwelling, **130–131**, 135–136

Vanadium, 186
Velella (sailors-by-the-wind), 20, **21**, **40**, 64
Veliger larvae, **57**, 58, 226
Vertebrate, defined, 226
Vertical migration, 88–91, 100–101, 103
Viperfish, **98–99**
Virgin Islands National Park, 205
Viscosity, 46, 67, 226

Walruses, **212**
Walsh, Don, 214–215
Wandering albatrosses, 12, **13**, 128
Water fleas, **55**
Weddell seals, **116–117**, 120
West Australian Current, *map* **23**
West Wind Drift, 20–21, *map* **22–23**, 113, 133, 135, 226
Whale sharks, **209**
Whalebone, **123**
Whales, 49, 66, 80–87, 144, **207**, 211, **213**
  Antarctic, 113, 119–126
  (*See also* Dolphins; Porpoises)
Whelks, 140–141, 189, **222**
White, Edward H., 35
White Cliffs of Dover, 195, 199
White sharks, **208**
White-tipped sharks, **74**
Wilson's petrels, **10–12**
Winds, 9–43, 135
  birds and, 9–18
  current rips and, 36–41, 43
  hurricane, 158
  migration and, 11, 12, 28–35
  red tides and, 136–137
  Sargasso Sea and, 24–26
  and types of currents, 20–21, *map* **22–23**
  (*See also* West Wind Drifts)
Winter, 110–112, 125, 142
Woods Hole Oceanographic Institution (Massachusetts), 28, 116
Worms, 26, 56, 72, 106, 187–189, 195
  in coral reefs, 165, 166
  eggs of, **108–109**
  in kelp beds, 140–142
Wrasses, **178–179**

Zoea larvae, **56**, 57, 226
Zooplankton, defined, 226